C000280826

Mathdonic

Gweithgareddau ar gyfer mathemateg yn y Blynyddoedd Cynnar, Cyfnod All\
ac addas i'w defnyddio fel cysylltiad rhwng CA2 a CA3

GÊMAU

Mae llawer o gêmau yn ymwneud â mathemateg, un ai yn uniongyrchol neu'n anuniongyrchol. Mae llawer o gêmau yn deillio o fathemateg. Gellir dyfeisio gêmau i gynorthwyo plant i ddysgu syniadau a chysyniadau mathemategol penodol. Mae llawer o blant ac oedolion yn gweld gêmau, o ryw fath neu'i gilydd, yn eithriadol ddiddorol. Mae'r rhifyn hwn o Mathdonic yn edrych ar bob math o gyfleoedd i ddefnyddio'r diddordeb hwn i ddatblygu sgiliau a dealltwriaeth fathemategol plant, boed hynny o fewn y dosbarth neu yn yr awyr agored.

Mae'n ddigon hawdd cael gafael ar fersiynau cyfrifiadurol o lawer o'r gêmau hyn heddiw, a gellir darganfod fersiynau am ddim drwy chwilota yn GOOGLE neu beiriannau archwilio tebyg. Fodd bynnag, ym marn yr awduron, y gêmau gwreiddiol yw'r gorau yn ddieithriad!

Cynnwys

Cyhoeddir **Mathdonic** ddwywaith y flwyddyn gan Ysgol Addysg, Prifysgol Cymru, Bangor a'r Ganolfan Astudiaethau Addysg, Prifysgol Cymru, Aberystwyth.
Gellir cael rhagor o gopïau o'r argraffiad hwn neu ôl-rifynnau gan CAA, Yr Hen Goleg, Aberystwyth, SY23 2AX (ffôn 01970 622121)

Pwyllgor golygyddol:
John Coleman, Yr Ysgol Addysg, Bangor
Siân Davies-Eliott, Cynnal
Helen Elis-Jones, Yr Ysgol Addysg, Bangor
Jen Evans, Ymarferydd Y Blynyddoedd Cynnar
Manon Harries, Cydlynydd Mathemateg, Ysgol Gynradd Machynlleth
Dylan Jones, Adran Addysg, Aberystwyth
Peter Moody, cyn Ymgynghorwr mathemateg, Dyfed

Maldwyn Pryse, AALl Powys
Dr Gareth Roberts, Yr Ysgol Addysg, Bangor
Helen Davies, Y Ganolfan Astudiaethau Addysg, Aberystwyth
Terwyn Tomos, AALl Ceredigion
Siôn Watkins, AALl Sir Gaerfyrddin

Ysgrifennwyd a chyfrannwyd tuag at y rhifyn hwn gan Helen Elis-Jones, Yr Ysgol Addysg, Bangor, Sally Francis, Heather Cale, Adelaide Jones, Annie Mustoe (Ysgol Fabanod Mount Airey), Bethan Cartwright, Ieuan Jones (Cynnal), Peter Moody.

Golygydd: Peter Moody
Dylunwyr: Enfys Jenkins / Andrew Gaunt
Argraffwyr: Cambria
ISBN: 1 85644 515 1
© ACCAC 2004

GÊMAU SIAPIAU

Bingo Siapiau

Cydosod rhai siapiau drwy adnabod elfennau sy'n debyg a chyfeiriad

Nod Dysgu Cynnar: Dosbarthu a chydosod gwrthrychau.

Maint grŵp: Hyd at 4 plentyn.

Beth sydd ei angen: Cardiau bwrdd Bingo, 'galwr' fydd yn 'galw' drwy ddefnyddio cardiau bingo unigol (wedi eu torri allan) neu ddis siapiau. Cownteri.

Chwarae'r gêm: Rhowch fwrdd bingo 4-siâp i bob plentyn (gweler enghreifftiau). Trafodwch ac enwch y siapiau y gallant eu gweld ar y bwrdd. Eglurwch y bydd y 'galwr' yn troi'r cardiau siapiau unigol drosodd, neu'n taflu'r dis siapiau ac yn galw enw'r siâp. Bydd yn rhaid i'r disgyblion adnabod y siâp ar eu bwrdd ac yna gosod cownter arno. Bydd y gêm yn mynd yn ei blaen nes bydd un plentyn wedi gorchuddio pob un o'r 4 siâp ac yn gweiddi 'Bingo!'

Cymorth a Gwaith Estynedig: Datblygwch y gêm drwy ddefnyddio gwahanol fathau o fyrddau bingo 'siapiau', e.e. lliwiwch y siapiau fel bo'n rhaid i'r plant gydosod lliw a siâp, neu defnyddiwch siapiau o wahanol feintiau hyd yn oed. Gallech ymestyn y gêm hefyd a chynnwys hyd at 6 siâp ar y bwrdd. Gallai hyn gynnwys amrywiaeth o ran lliw a/neu faint.

Byrddau Chwarae Bingo

Loto 'siapiau'

Dewiswch siâp ag enw arbennig

Nod Dysgu Cynnar: Defnyddio iaith i ddisgrifio siapiau fflat.

Maint grŵp: Gwaith grŵp o 4 i 6 o blant.

Beth sydd ei angen: Cardiau bwrdd bingo o'r dasg uchod, cardiau bingo unigol neu ddis siapiau. Cownteri.

Chwarae'r gêm: Rhowch gerdyn bwrdd bingo i bob plentyn ac eglurwch mai nod y gêm yw ceisio cydosod y siapiau ar y bwrdd o flaen pawb arall, un ai drwy godi cardiau unigol neu drwy daflu dis siapiau. Yr enillydd yw'r cyntaf i guddio ei 4 siâp un ai â'r cardiau siapiau unigol neu'r cownteri os defnyddir y dis.

Cymorth a Gwaith Estynedig: Wrth i'r plant fagu hyder wrth chwarae'r gêm gellir cynnwys mwy o siapiau ar y cerdyn bwrdd bingo a gellir cynnwys mwy o nodweddion siapiau, ee. siâp, lliw a maint. Gellir chwarae'r gêm hefyd o chwith, h.y. y plant yn dechrau â'r cardiau/cownteri ar eu byrddau a'r cyntaf i dynnu pob un o'i gardiau/gownteri yw'r enillydd.

Siapiau lolipop

Dechrau defnyddio'r enwau mathemategol ar gyfer siapiau 2D 'fflat' a thermau mathemategol i ddisgrifio siapiau.

Nod Dysgu Cynnar: Defnyddio syniadau a dulliau mathemategol sy'n datblygu i ddatrys problemau ymarferol.

Maint grŵp: Dosbarth cyfan a/neu grwpiau bychain.

Cyfarpar: Paratowch set o siapiau lolipop ymlaen llaw. Gwnewch y rhain drwy lynu siâp sylfaenol (sgwâr, cylch, petryal, triongl) ar ffon lolipop neu rywbeth tebyg. Gall maint a lliw y siapiau amrywio.

Chwarae'r gêm: Dangoswch y set o ffyn lolipop i'r plant a thrafodwch y gwahanol liwiau, meintiau a siapiau. Rhowch 6 o'r ffyn i unigolion a gofynnwch i'r plant hyn sefyll o flaen y dosbarth fel bo pawb yn gallu gweld eu siapiau. Eglurwch fod yn rhaid i'r plant ddal eu ffon i fyny yn uchel os yw eu siâp hwy yn cyd-fynd â meini prawf y cwestiwn, h.y. codwch eich ffon os yw eich siâp yn gylch... Gofynnwch nifer o wahanol gwestiynau i sicrhau fod y plant i gyd yn deall pryd y dylent godi eu ffon i fyny yn uchel!

Cymorth a Gwaith Estynedig: Gallai'r cwestiynau amrywiol fod yn seiliedig ar:

siâp, maint neu liw codwch eich ffon os yw eich siâp yn felyn,

siâp a maint neu siâp a lliw neu maint a lliw codwch eich ffon os yw eich siâp yn las ac yn driongl

siâp, maint a lliw codwch eich ffon os yw eich siâp yn goch, yn fawr ac yn betryal

defnyddio nodweddion negyddol codwch eich ffon os yw eich siâp yn driongl sydd heb fod yn las!

Holwch y plant ynglŷn â sut y maen nhw'n ymateb i'r cwestiynau a ofynnir iddynt.

Siapiau Cerddorol

Dangos chwilfrydedd a sylwgarwch wrth sôn am siapiau, sut y maen nhw'n ymdebygu i'w gilydd neu pam y maen nhw'n wahanol.

Nod Dysgu Cynnar: Trafod, adnabod ac ail-greu patrymau syml.

Maint grŵp: Dosbarth cyfan a/neu grwpiau bychain.

Cyfarpar: Bydd arnoch angen amryw o sgwariau, petryalau, cylchoedd a thrionglau mawr wedi eu torri o bapur. Chwaraewr casetiau a thâp cerddoriaeth addas.

Chwarae'r gêm: Cyflwynwch y siapiau papur i'r disgyblion drwy dynnu eu sylw at nodweddion y gwahanol siapiau. Defnyddiwch gwestiynau a thermau megis *nifer yr ochrau syth, nifer y corneli, pa un yw'r ochr hwyaf/fyrraf ... siâp, syth, crwn, cornel, ymyl, ochr ...* Gosodwch y siapiau papur ar lawr y dosbarth gan sicrhau fod digon o le, a gwneud mwy o le yn y dosbarth os bydd angen. Dewiswch 5 o blant i fynd i eistedd ar y 5 siâp sgwâr gwahanol, trowch y gerddoriaeth ymlaen, a phan fydd y gerddoriaeth yn stopio bydd yn rhaid i'r plant ddarganfod, adnabod ac eistedd ar sgwâr papur. Daliwch ati i chwarae'r gêm, gan ddewis gwahanol siapiau cychwynnol a gofalu fod y plant i gyd yn cael cyfle i chwarae.

Cymorth a Gwaith Estynedig: Gellir gwneud y gêm yn haws i'r plant, a'u helpu i adnabod y gwahanol siapiau, drwy sicrhau fod pob sgwâr yn cael ei liwio'n goch, pob triongl yn cael ei liwio'n las... Yn hytrach na darganfod yr un siâp cychwynnol bob tro, gallai'r plant eistedd yn gyntaf ar siâp sgwâr, yna ar siâp triongl, ac yna ar siâp cylch ... Gallai'r plant hefyd sefyll, hopian, neu neidio ar y siâp dan sylw yn hytrach na dim ond eistedd arno! Yn wahanol i'r gêm 'Cadeiriau Cerddorol' (Musical Chairs) nid oes rhaid lleihau nifer y siapiau ac felly nid oes neb yn ennill nac yn colli.

I ble mae'n perthyn?

Mae hyn yn rhoi cyfle i'r plant ddangos hyder a chynnig atebion i broblemau

Nod Dysgu Cynnar: Dosbarthu a chydosod gwrthrychau.
Defnyddio iaith i ddisgrifio siapiau.

Maint grŵp: Grwpiau bychain.

Cyfarpar: Siapiau papur (gweler Siapiau Cerddorol) neu amlinelliadau pedwar siâp sylfaenol, bag â llinyn tynnu, set o siapiau 2D.

Chwarae'r gêm: Gosodwch gylch papur ar y bwrdd a gofynnwch i bob plentyn, yn ei dro, deimlo'r bag a thynnu siâp cylch ohono. Eglurwch na allant edrych yn y bag ac y bydd yn rhaid iddynt ddarganfod y siâp drwy ei deimlo. Anogwch y plant i feddwl am nodweddion y siâp a ddewiswyd - a fydd gan y siâp gorneli, ymylon syth, ymylon crwm ...? Gwnewch y gweithgaredd eto ar gyfer y siapiau sylfaenol eraill. Gwnewch y gweithgaredd eto drwy ddefnyddio siapiau 3D yn hytrach na siapiau 2D. Unwaith eto anogwch y plant i deimlo gwahanol nodweddion y siapiau.

Cymorth a Gwaith Estynedig: Mae'n bosibl gwneud y gweithgaredd eto drwy ddefnyddio siapiau 3D yn hytrach na siapiau 2D. Unwaith eto anogwch y plant i deimlo gwahanol nodweddion y siapiau. Efallai y gallai plant iau ddewis siapiau sy'n rholio/siapiau ag ymylon syth/siapiau sydd â chorneli, yn hytrach na siapiau ag enwau penodol.

GÊMAU AR YR IARD CHWARAE

Daw'r symbyliad ar gyfer y dilyniant hwn o weithgareddau o'r syniad o fynd â'r cwricwlwm allan i'r awyr agored. Mae ffyrdd o ddefnyddio gweithgareddau awyr agored i hybu dysgu yn y dosbarth wedi bodoli erioed. Erbyn hyn mae'r pwyslais wedi symud tuag at ddefnyddio'r awyr agored fel man cychwyn.

Rydym wedi edrych ar hyn o ddau safbwynt, gan ddefnyddio adnoddau sy'n bodoli ac addasu'r rhai sydd gennym, i gwrdd ag anghenion penodol. Mae gan bob ysgol fannau chwarae 'llawr caled' o wahanol feintiau, a rydym wedi defnyddio hyn fel y man gweithio craidd.

Mae'r syniadau yn syrthio, yn fras, i ddau gategori. Ar y naill law ceir rhigymau a gêmau y gellir eu defnyddio yn fathematgol allan yn yr iard ac ar y llaw arall ceir gweithgareddau sy'n seiliedig ar yr iard fathemategol yn uniongyrchol.

Os yw'n bwrw glaw, gellir chwarae llawer o'r gêmau hyn yn y Neuadd, ac eithrio'r gêmau lle defnyddir marciau arbennig (oni bai eich bod yn eu peintio ar lawr eich Neuadd hefyd!)

5

Gweithgareddau	Ystod Oedran	Amcanion Dysgu Mathemateg	Adnoddau	Sgiliau Allweddol	Cysylliadau â'r cwricwlwm
1. Ddefaid bach, dowch adref Arweinydd: Ddefaid bach dowch adref, Grŵp: Mê!, mae arnom ofn! Arweinydd: Mae'r blaidd wedi mynd i ffwrdd am hir Ddefaid bach dowch adref. …Dowch adref fesul 2, 3, 4, etc. Mae'r arweinydd a'r plant yn adrodd y rhigwm uchod ac yna mae'r athro/athrawes neu'r arweinydd yn dweud "Dewch adref fesul ___". Yna mae'n rhaid i'r plant ffurfio grwpiau o'r nifer dan sylw a rhedeg at yr arweinydd. Y plant sydd ar ôl yw'r gweddill ac maen nhw'n eistedd i lawr hyd at ddiwedd y gêm.	Derb –Bl2	Chwarae gêmau. Gweithio ar y cyd. Adrodd rhigwm. Rhannu set gyfan yn is-setiau llai. Deall y term "gweddill".	Iard chwarae	Cyfathrebu Cydweithredu Sgiliau mathemategol Sgiliau gwrando	Mathemateg Addysg Gorfforol ABCh Saesneg: Llefaredd
2. Anfonais lythyr i Lili fwyn Anfonais lythyr i Lili fwyn Ac ar y ffordd fe'i collais. Mae un ohonoch wedi'i ddwyn A'i guddio yn eich poced. Na, nid ti, na nid ti, na nid ti … (Yn y gêm draddodiadol, mae'r plant yn eistedd mewn cylch. Dewisir un plentyn i gerdded o amgylch y cylch tra bydd y rhigwm yn cael ei adrodd. Mae'r plentyn yn dal i fynd yn ei flaen ac yna'n gollwng hances y tu ôl i un o'r plant sy'n eistedd ar lawr ac yna mae'n gweiddi: "Ti oedd o". Yna mae'r disgybl cyntaf a ddewiswyd yn rhedeg o amgylch y tu allan i'r cylch ar ôl y chwaraewr cyntaf. Mae'r un a fydd yn dychwelyd gyntaf i'r lle gwag yn sefyll yno. Mae'r gêm yn mynd yn ei blaen â'r plentyn arall yn cerdded o amgylch y cylch.) Gellir newid y gêm fel bo'r plant yn gorfod ymateb i rifau. Rhoddir un neu fwy o gardiau rhif i'r plant wrth iddynt eistedd yn y cylch. Gellir newid y rhigwm i rywbeth fel hyn: Anfonais rif i'm hannwyl ffrind … A'i guddio yn eich poced. Y lleidr yw rhif ___. Yna mae'r plant yn edrych ar eu rhif/rhifau. Os yw'r rhif hwnnw gan un ohonynt, rhaid iddo sefyll a cheisio curo'r 'galwr' wrth redeg yn ôl i'w le o'i flaen. Syniadau gwahaniaethol: **Blynyddoedd Cynnar:** Adnabod rhifau hyd at 10/20. **Blwyddyn 1:** Adnabod rhifau hyd at 20/50+. "Rhif rhwng 4 a 6." etc "Eilrif sy'n llai na 4." "Rhif a wneir drwy adio 6 + 4." "Rhif sydd yn 1 deg a 3 uned." **Blwyddyn 2:** Datblygu'r uchod a hefyd: 1. Adnabod rhifau hyd at 100+. 2. Rhif sy'n cynmwys 2 gant, 3 deg a 7 uned. Amrediad o gardiau lle gellid cael problemau cildroi, i wirio dealltwriaeth o werth lle, e.e. 432, 234, 423, 324, 342, 243 etc.	Blynyddoedd Cynnar – Yr1	Chwarae gêmau. Gweithio ar y cyd. Adrodd rhigwm. Gwybod rhifau hyd at 10/20/30/50/100+. Adnabod a darllen rhifau. Gwybod odrifau ac eilrifau. Deall gwerth lle. Gwybod bondiau rhif.	Iard chwarae Llythyr Rhifau	Cyfathrebu Cydweithio Sgiliau mathemategol	Addysg Gorfforol Mathemateg ABCh Saesneg: Llefaredd

6

Gweithgareddau	Blynyddoedd	Chwarae gêmau	Clociau arddangos	Cyfathrebu	Mathemateg
"Hicori Dicori Doc" & "Faint o'r gloch, Mr Blaidd?" **Hicori Dicori Doc** Hicori Dicori Doc Llygoden lan y cloc. Mae'n taro tri I lawr â hi. Hicori Dicori Doc. Gellir newid y rhif yn y rhigwm a bob tro yr adroddir y rhigwm, dewisir dau blentyn i ddangos faint o'r gloch yw hi ar y cloc drwy gymryd arnynt eu bod yn fysedd. Gellir defnyddio prennau mesur metr os dymunir. Gellir defnyddio wyneb cloc mawr i ddangos faint o'r gloch yw hi a gofyn i'r plant adnabod yr amser ar y cloc i gwblhau'r rhigwm. **Faint o'r gloch, Mr Blaidd?** Mae'r plant yn sefyll mewn rhes yn wynebu'r athro/athrawes (neu blentyn) ym mhen arall y buarth. Mae'r plant yn dweud "Faint o'r gloch, Mr Blaidd?" ac yn y gêm draddodiadol mae'r athro/athrawes yn ateb: "Mae hi'n 3 o'r gloch". Yna mae'r plant yn cymryd 3 cham ymlaen. Chwaraewch y gêm nes bydd rhywun yn ennill drwy gyrraedd yr athro/athrawes. Os yw'r athro/athrawes yn ateb "Amser Cinio" bydd y plant i gyd yn gorfod rhedeg yn ôl i'r man cychwyn. Datblygwch y gêm drwy gyflwyno cloc mawr sy'n caniatáu i'r plant ddarllen faint o'r gloch yw hi a chymryd y nifer cywir o gamau. Defnyddiwch gloc digidol gyda phlant mwy galluog.	Cynnar – Blwyddyn 2	Gweithio ar y cyd. Adrodd rhigwm. Darllen clociau analog a digidol.	Clociau arddangos Prennau mesur metr Clociau i'w defnyddio ar y buarth	Cyfathrebu Cydweithio Sgiliau mathemategol Sgiliau gwrando	Mathemateg Addysg Gorfforol ABCh Saesneg: Llefaredd TGCh: Meddalwedd Dysgu Faint o'r Gloch
4. I mewn ac allan rhwng y blodau I mewn ac allan rhwng y blodau (x3) Hei Hei Di Ho. Taro ysgwydd merch neu fachgen (x3) Hei Hei Di Ho. (Ailadrodd) Mae'r plant yn sefyll mewn cylch ac yn gafael yn nwylo ei gilydd â'u breichiau i fyny. Dewisir un plentyn i fynd i mewn ac allan o amgylch y cylch wrth i'r rhigwm gael ei adrodd. Pan fydd y rhigwm yn cyrraedd "Taro ysgwydd…" mae'r plentyn yn aros y tu ôl i blentyn ac yn ei daro'n ysgafn ar ei ysgwydd nes daw'r rhigwm i ben. Yna mae'r plentyn newydd hwn yn gafael yn llaw y plentyn cyntaf a gellir gofyn cwestiynau megis "Faint sydd nawr?" a "Beth yw 1 yn fwy na____?" Mae'r gêm yn dal i fynd yn ei blaen nes bydd mwy o blant yn y rhes sy'n mynd i mewn ac allan nag sydd yn y cylch ei hun. **Mae'r Ffermwr yn ei gae** Mae'r Ffermwr yn ei gae Mae'r Ffermwr yn ei gae Ei Ai Adio Mae'r Ffermwr yn ei gae: Mae'r ffermwr eisiau gwraig, etc. Mae'r wraig eisiau babi, etc. Mae'r babi eisiau nyrs, etc. Mae'r nyrs eisiau ci, etc. Mae'r ci eisiau asgwrn, etc. Mae pawb yn taro'r asgwrn, etc. Mae'r plant yn sefyll mewn cylch ac mae'r plentyn sydd wedi ei ddewis i fod yn ffermwr yn sefyll yn y canol. Mae'r plant yn cerdded o amgylch y ffermwr, gan adrodd neu ganu'r rhigwm. Yna mae'r ffermwr yn dewis gwraig ac mae'r ail bennill yn cael ei ganu. Mae hyn yn dal i fynd yn ei flaen gan ddilyn yr un patrwm tan y pennill 'Mae pawb yn taro'r asgwrn' pan ddaw pawb yn y cylch ymlaen i gyffwrdd yr asgwrn yn ysgafn. Bob tro bydd pennill yn cael ei adrodd neu ei ganu ceir cyfleoedd i ofyn "Faint sydd yn y cylch? Faint sydd nawr? Beth am adio 1 arall?" etc.	Cynnar – Blwyddyn 1	Chwarae gêmau. Chwarae ar y cyd. Adrodd rhigwm. Adio 1 arall. Dilyn cyfarwyddiadau.	Iard chwarae	Cyfathrebu Cydweithio Sgiliau mathemategol Sgiliau gwrando	Mathemateg Addysg Gorfforol ABCh

Gweithgareddau	Ystod Oedran	Amcanion Dysgu Mathemateg	Adnoddau	Sgiliau Allweddol	Cysylliadau â'r cwricwlwm
5. Gêmau sgipio Mae dau blentyn yn troi'r rhaff tra mae plentyn arall yn sgipio y tu mewn iddi. "Fi yw'r car bach cyflym, rhif dau gant a chwech Mi es i rownd y gornel… (Wrth ddweud y llinell hon mae'r un sy'n sgipio yn rhedeg allan o'r rhaff, ac yn mynd o gwmpas, y tu ôl i un o'r rhai sy'n troi'r rhaff, ac yna yn ôl i mewn i sgipio o'r ochr arall.) …Mi stopiais wrth y golau A phwyso ar y brêc Fe'm daliwyd gan y plismon A'm rhoi yn y jêl Faint o flynyddoedd fûm i yno? 1,2,3… Daliwch ati nes bydd yr un sy'n sgipio 'allan'. Gellir newid y geiriau yn ôl y galw. Gellir newid y rhifau ar y diwedd yn batrymau rhifau, e.e. 2,4,6,8 neu 5,10,15,20 etc.	Bl 1/2	Cymryd rhan mewn gêm sgipio. Gweithio gyda'i gilydd. Cyfrif hyd at 10+. Cyfrif fesul 2.	Rhaffau sgipio Rhigwm	Cyfathrebu Cydweithio Cyfrif Sgiliau mathemateg	Addysg Gorfforol ABCh Saesneg: Llefaredd
6. Rhifau hyd at 100 – o amgylch ymyl y buarth **Blynyddoedd Cynnar** 1. Cyfrif wrth ganu, cyn belled ag y gallwch. 2. Cyfrif gyda phartner mwy galluog. **Blwyddyn 1/2** Cyfrif o amgylch y cylch yn unigol neu mewn parau Cyfrif ymlaen ac yn ôl Defnyddio llinell i adio neu dynnu Cyfrif fesul 2 etc o 1 neu unrhyw rif a roddir, e.e. patrymau odrifol neu eilrifol. Sefyll ar rif rhwng ____ a ____. Sefyll ar luosrif 2, 5, 10 etc. Sefyll ar luosrif 2 a 5.	Blynyddoedd Cynnar – Blwyddyn 2	Cyfrif ymlaen fesul 1 o unrhyw rif a roddir. Cyfrif yn ôl fesul 1 o unrhyw rif a roddir. Cyfrif ymlaen neu yn ôl fesul 2, 3, 4, 5 a 10.	Rhifau yn yr iard chwarae	Cyfathrebu Cydweithio Sgiliau mathemateg Sgiliau gwrando	Mathemateg
7. Gêmau Drysfa/Crwydryn (Roamer) i'w chwarae yn yr Awyr Agored Defnyddiwch ddrysfa wag i gynllunio llwybr neu defnyddiwch saethau i wneud llwybr gan amcangyfrif sawl cam i'r chwith neu i'r dde sydd ei angen. Bydd angen i'r plant gofnodi syniadau a gwirio'r llwybr cyn gofyn i eraill ei ddilyn. Rhowch fwgwd dros lygaid un plentyn a rhowch gyfarwyddiadau iddo i'w dilyn. Rhaglennwch y Crwydryn i ddilyn y llwybr, e.e. camau, ymlaen, i'r chwith ac i'r dde. Mae saethau laminedig wedi eu gosod ar y ddrysfa yn creu llwybr syml y gall plant iau ei ddilyn a hefyd gall hyn helpu rhai plant i gofio pa gamau i'w cofnodi. **Grid Drysfa Rifau Heb Ei Lenwi** Rhowch rifau mewn sgwariau ar y ddrysfa. Gofynnwch i'r plant ddefnyddio'r llwybrau i ddarganfod ffyrdd: 1. Gan wneud llwybr sy'n rhoi'r cyfanswm lleiaf, mwyaf. 2. Darganfod llwybr sy'n rhoi cyfanswm odrifol/eilrifol. 3. Darganfod llwybr sy'n cynhyrchu cyfanswm penodol. 4. Sawl cyfanswm gwahanol allwch chi ei wneud? Sut ydych chi'n gwybod eich bod wedi cynhyrchu'r holl gyfansymiau posibl?	Blynyddoedd Cynnar – Bl 2+	Dilyn llwybr. Ysgrifennu cyfarwyddiadau. Rhoi cyfarwyddiadau. Dilyn cyfarwyddiadau. Amcangyfrif hyd. Datrys problemau. Ymchwilio i rifau. Adio rhifau.	Crwydryn (Roamer) Drysfa buarth (heb ei llenwi) Papur i gofnodi Drysfa buarth (heb ei llenwi) Sialc	Cyfathrebu Cydweithio Datrys problemau Ymchwilio Sgiliau mathemategol	Mathemateg Daearyddiaeth

	Blwyddyn 1/2	Chwarae ar y cyd. Cyfrif rhifau. Cyfrif ymlaen. Gwneud symiau adio a thynnu.	Sgwâr 100 iard chwarae Rhaffau sgipio Dis Sgwâr 100 ar bapur (tudalen 16)	Cyfathrebu Cydweithio Cyfrif Sgiliau mathemategol	Mathemateg ABCh
8. Nadroedd ac ysgolion Defnyddio sgwâr 100 iard chwarae a rhaffau sgipio i wneud Nadroedd ac Ysgolion. Defnyddiwch ddis mawr meddal a chwaraewch y gêm yn y ffordd arferol neu drwy ddefnyddio'r amrywiadau canlynol. Taflwch 2 ddis ac adiwch y rhifau. Taflwch ddau ddis, un â rhifau mawr a'r llall â rhifau bychain – tynnwch y rhif bychan o'r rhif mawr a bydd y canlyniad yn rhoi nifer y camau a gymerir. Dewiswch rif o fag. **Defnyddio sgwâr 100 i chwarae gêmau cyfrif.** 1. Cyfrif fesul 1, 2, 3, etc o 1 neu unrhyw rif a roddir 2. Odrifau ac eilrifau Sefwch ar rif sy'n llai na... Sefwch ar unrhyw rif rhwng... ac... Sefwch ar unrhyw rif ac adiwch eich rhif at rif ffrind – a fydd y ddau/ddwy ohonoch yn gallu sefyll ar y rhif newydd?					
9. Cwmpawd (Os gellir lliwio'r cwmpawd â phaent/sialc i ddangos lleoliad cywir yr ysgol, mae'n ddefnyddiol gyda golwg ar ddaearyddiaeth hefyd.) Sefwch ar y Gogledd, De, Dwyrain, Gorllewin, etc. Ble mae'r De Orllewin, Gogledd Ddwyrain, etc? Sefwch ar y Gogledd – trowch drwy onglau sgwâr i'r dde ac i'r chwith – hanner ongl sgwâr, etc. Ym mhle ydych chi yn awr? Beth allwch chi ei weld i'r Gogledd o'r ysgol? Beth sydd gyferbyn â'r De Ddwyrain? etc.	Bl. 1/2	Defnyddio cwmpawd. Gwybod pwyntiau'r cwmpawd. Trafod cyfeiriad.	Cwmpawd Cwmpawd iard chwarae	Cyfathrebu Cydweithio Sgiliau mathemategol Sgiliau ymchwilio	Mathemateg Daearyddiaeth
10. Cloc Ymchwilio i amser drwy ddefnyddio prennau mesur metr neu ddau blentyn fel 'bysedd'. Faint o'r gloch yw hi? Defnyddio cloc mawr i ddangos amser sy'n cyfateb. Faint o'r gloch fydd hi mewn 1 awr? Dangoswch hyn ar y cloc.	Blynyddoedd Cynnar hyd at Fl. 2	Gwybod sut i ddweud faint o'r gloch yw hi gan ddefnyddio clociau analog. Darllen clociau. Cydosod clociau.	Clociau Clociau iard chwarae	Cyfathrebu Cydweithio Sgiliau mathemategol Sgiliau ymchwilio	Mathemateg ABCh
11. Hopsgots Fesul un, taflwch fag ffa ar rif 1 a hopian, neidio ar yr holl rifau eraill ac yn ôl. Wedyn, gwnewch yr un peth â'r rhif 2 ar goll. Gwnewch yr un peth â'r rhifau nesaf yn eu trefn. Gellir newid y rhifau yn rhifau mwy ac nid oes rhaid eu gosod yn eu trefn. Yma felly yr her fydd hopian a neidio yn y drefn gywir. Gellir awgrymu gwahanol ddilyniannau o rifau hefyd fel bo'n rhaid i'r plant ddilyn eilrifau er enghraifft.	Blynyddoedd Cynnar – Blwyddyn 2.	Gwybod rhifau hyd at 10+. Defnyddio rhifau sydd ar goll. Dilyn dilyniant.	Grid Hopsgots Sialc Bagiau ffa Gridiau gwag ar gyfer adio gyda rhifau sydd ar goll (Taflen waith 1, tudalen 12)	Cyfathrebu Cydweithio Sgiliau mathemategol	Mathemateg Addysg Gorfforol
12. Llinell rif wag 1. Rhoi rhifau ar linell rif yn y drefn gywir. 2. Defnyddio llinell rif ar gyfer adio gyda rhifau penodol yn eu lle. 3. Llinellau rhif wedi eu llunio'n rhannol – llenwch y rhifau sydd ar goll. 4. Taflu dis o rifau a roddir arno.	Blynyddoedd Cynnar – Bl 2	Gwybod rhifau hyd at 10/20/50/100. Trefnu rhifau ar linell rif. Darganfod rhifau sydd ar goll.	Cardiau rhif Dis	Cyfathrebu Cydweithio Sgiliau mathemategol	Mathemateg

Gweithgareddau	Ystod Oedran	Amcanion Dysgu Mathemateg	Adnoddau	Sgiliau Allweddol	Cysylltiadau â'r cwricwlwm
13. Cymesuredd cylchdro siapiau 2D Siapiau 2D wedi eu peintio ar yr iard. Defnyddio siapiau mawr i'w gosod dros yr amlinelliadau sy'n perthyn. Defnyddio drychau, cardiau drych, etc i archwilio cymesuredd. Sut y mae'r siapiau hyn yn cylchdroi? A ydynt yn edrych yr un fath wrth iddynt gylchdroi drwy 90 gradd neu droad? Trafodwch onglau sgwâr. Sut y mae'r siapiau yn newid? Ym mhle mae'r corneli yn awr? Etc. **Llenwi siapiau gwag** Gofynnwch i'r plant lenwi siâp gwag ag amrediad o ddeunyddiau. Sawl bricsen fydd ei hangen arnoch i'w lenwi, etc? - Llenwch â briciau mawr – Sawl un? - Llenwch amrediad o siapiau rheolaidd gwag. - Sawl bricsen sy'n llenwi sail? – trafodwch siapiau sy'n brithweithio. - Diffinio lle gwag ar y llawr gan ddefnyddio sialc neu baent, etc. Sawl siâp, e.e. ciwboidau, briciau, etc fydd yn llenwi'r lle gwag? - Cymharu'r defnydd o giwbiau a chiwboidau. - Sawl siâp bychan sydd ei angen arnoch i wneud siâp mawr? Sawl ciwb fydd yn gwneud siâp mwy? Sawl ciwb fydd yn llenwi'r un siâp gwag oedd yn cael ei lenwi gan y ciwboidau? - Sut allwn ni ddefnyddio'r un nifer o flociau eto heb fynd dros y llinellau? e.e. llumio haenau. Archwilio haenau a'r niferoedd dan sylw. - Defnyddio pwll tywod i gysylltu â chynhwysedd – llenwi cynwysyddion, etc. Tynnu lluniau siapiau 2D a 3D o amgylch yr ysgol gan ddefnyddio camera digidol.	Blynyddoedd Cynnar – Blwyddyn 2	Enwi siapiau 2D. Cydosod siapiau 2D. Defnyddio siapiau 2D. Ymchwilio i siapiau sy'n cylchdroi. Defnyddio troad ongl sgwâr mewn tasg ymarferol. Llenwi lle gwag â chiwbiau. Amcangyfrif arwynebedd. Archwilio siâp. Astudio brithwaith.	Siapiau ar iard chwarae Siapiau sy'n cyd-fynd â'i gilydd ac sy'n cylchdroi (gweler Taflen waith 2, tudalen 13) Drychau Blociau mawr a bach Sialc, paent, llinyn, etc i ddiffinio lle gwag Siapiau i'w llenwi (Taflen waith 3, tudalen 14)	Cyfathrebu Cydweithio Sgiliau mathemateg Datrys problemau Ymchwilio	Mathemateg ABCh
14. Cylchau Defnyddiwch amrediad o wahanol feintiau a lliwiau a'u gosod ar hap ar yr iard. Gwrando ar gyfarwyddiadau ac gyfarwyddiadau, e.e. sefwch y tu mewn, y tu allan i gylchau o feintiau a siapiau gwahanol. Nodweddion: lliw, maint. Sefyll gyda ffrindiau yn y rhif cywir, e.e. "melyn 3" rhaid i dri phlentyn sefyll mewn cylch melyn. Gwaith estynedig: taflu bagiau ffa i'r cylchau sy'n cyfateb o ran rhif. Llwybrau o gylchau – symud o un i'r llall mewn dilyniant o rifau, o liwiau, etc. Dangos cardiau lliw a thrafod gwahanol 'symudiadau'. Eu harddangos er mwyn gallu cyfeirio atynt, e.e. Cyrraedd cylch coch a hopian, cyrraedd cylch gwyrdd a neidio, cyrraedd cylch glas a'i roi dros eich pen, etc. Datblygu i: Dilyniant o symudiadau, e.e. 3 naid, 2 hop. Timau – perfformio dilyniant o symudiadau gan ddefnyddio'r cylchau. **Adio rhifau** Gosodwch rif gwahanol ym mhob cylch. Rhoddir 3 bag ffa i bob plentyn ac mae'n rhaid iddo eu taflu i mewn i'r cylchau. Cofnodwch y sgorau. Rhowch sawl cynnig i bob plentyn a chofnodi ar siart. Archwiliwch "Sut y gallwn wneud y rhif mwyaf/lleiaf?" Gall rhifau wahaniaethu yn ôl gallu ac oedran.	Blynyddoedd Cynnar – Blwyddyn 2	Gwrando ar gyfarwyddiadau i ymateb yn briodol. Datblygu'r cysylltiad rhif-lliw. Ymateb yn briodol i wybodaeth ddarluniadol. Adnabod rhifau.	Cylchynau gwahanol liw o 2 faint. Cardiau lliwiau. Cardiau rhifau. (Taflen waith 4, tudalen 15)	Dilyn cyfarwyddiadau Geirfa safleol Ymwybyddiaeth ofodol Rheolaeth symudol bras Newid cyfeiriad a buanedd	Mathemateg Addysg Gorfforol Cwricwlwm Awyr Agored

15. Bwcedi a bagiau ffa 1. Cyfrif nifer y bwcedi a gosod rhifau mewn dilyniant o 0 – 10 . 2. Taflu bagiau ffa mewn trefn o 0 –10. 3. Gellid cydosod bagiau ffa sydd wedi eu rhifo â bwcedi sydd wedi eu rhifo. 4. Taflu ar hap – cyfrif y sgorau. 5. Taflu'r nifer cywir o fagiau ffa i fwced â rhif arno, e.e. bwced rhif 4 – taflwch 4 bag ffa i mewn iddo. Gwiriwch bob bwced i sicrhau fod y nifer cyfatebol o fagiau ffa ynddo. Edrychwch ar y set wag ym mwced 0. Os nad yw hyn yn gywir – Faint mwy neu faint llai sydd ei angen? 6. Bondiau rhif hyd at 5/10, etc – gwneud pump drwy daflu 2 fag ffa, gwaith pâr, neu waith unigol. Datblygwch gan ddefnyddio bondiau rhif eraill hyd at 10. 7. Pa dîm sy'n gallu darganfod y nifer mwyaf o ffyrdd o wneud 5, etc. 8. Taflu odrifau ac eilrifau – Allwch chi daflu 2/3 bag ffa i wneud eilrif? Archwiliwch y syniad. 9. Newidiwch y lleoliad a'r pellter i ddarganfod a yw'r posibilrwydd o lwyddo yn fwy ynteu llai. Sut y gellir cofnodi'r canlyniadau? Gall y plant daflu o wahanol bellterau ac onglau. Byddai defnyddio bagiau ffa lliw yn rhoi cyfleoedd i wneud gwahanol drynewidion.	Blynyddoedd Cynnar – Blwyddyn 2	Gosod rhifau mewn dilyniant 0 –10. Gwybod bondiau rhif hyd at 10. Ymchwilio i broblemau â rhifau.	Bwcedi wedi eu rhifo o 0 –10 (Gellir defnyddio gwahanol rifau). Bagiau ffa gwahanol liw	Gosod mewn dilyniant Trefnu Ymchwilio Datrys problemau A yw'r plant yn gallu eu cywiro eu hunain a gwerthuso eu llwyddiant personol? Gwerthuso drwy ganlyniad a sgiliau cyfathrebu.	Mathemateg ABCh Addysg Gorfforol
16.Llwybr o amgylch iard ac adeiladau'r ysgol Gan y bydd pob ysgol yn wahanol bydd llwybrau yn wahanol ym mhob achos. Gallai plant hŷn gynllunio llwybr i blant iau. Gallai syniadau posibl gynnwys: 1. Dilyn saethau o amgylch yr ysgol. 2. Llwybr Tedi bêr – cael hyd i 'Tedi' drwy ddilyn saethau cyfeiriadol neu drwy ddilyn cyfarwyddiadau, e.e. 2 gam ymlaen, 3 cham i'r dde. Yna gosodwch Tedi i sefyll ar y buarth: Beth mae o'n gallu ei weld o amrediad o leoliadau? Pa leoliad fyddai'r mwyaf diddorol iddo? 3. Llinellau sialc, etc. 4. Cerdded i mewn ac allan rhwng conau. 5. Dilyn cyfarwyddiadau ysgrifenedig. 6. Defnyddio lluniau neu ffotograffau er mwyn adnabod.	Blynyddoedd Cynnar – Blwyddyn 2 Blwyddyn 1/2	Dilyn cyfarwyddiadau. Dilyn llwybr. Archwilio tir yr ysgol. Rhoi cyfarwyddiadau.	Iard chwarae'r ysgol	Gwrando Ymchwilio Cyfathrebu Sgiliau mathemategol	Mathemateg TGCh ABCh Daearyddiaeth
17. Mesur gan ddefnyddio prennau mesur metr 1. Pa mor hir/llydan yw'r buarth? 2. Sawl cam yw hyn? 3. Sawl 'troed' yw'r hyd, un o flaen y llall? 4. Sawl plentyn sy'n ffitio ar hyd yr iard chwarae?		Defnyddio prennau mesur metr i fesur. Mesur gan ddefnyddio mesurau ansafonol. Mesur gan ddefnyddio mesurau safonol.	Prennau mesur metr	Cyfathrebu Cydweithio Sgiliau mathemategol Ymchwilio	Mathemateg

TAFLEN WAITH 1

(Cysylltiedig â Hopsgots rhifau sydd ar goll 11 tudalen 9.)

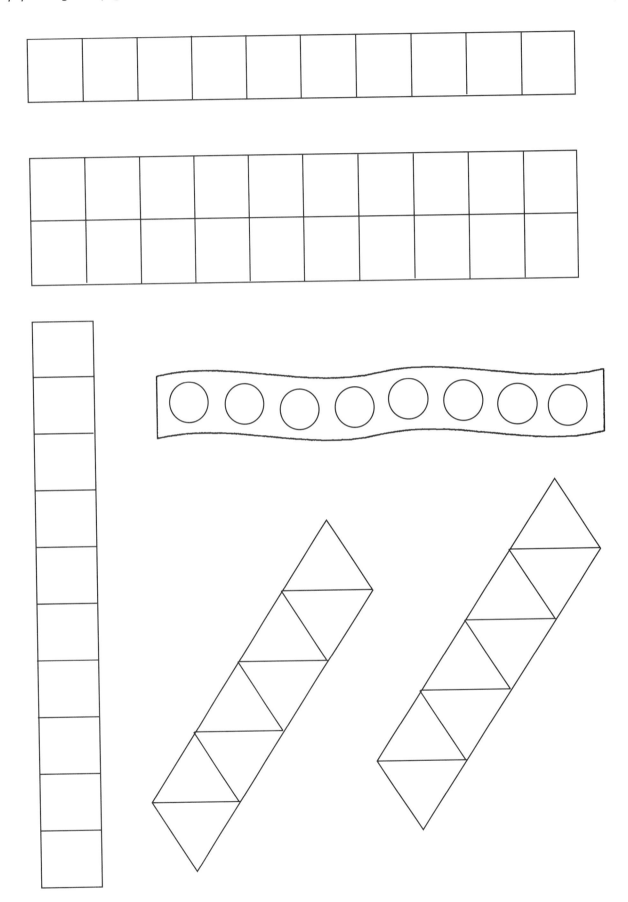

TAFLEN WAITH 2

(Cysylltiedig â siapiau 2D 13 tudalen 10) Mae pob siâp ym mhob rhes yn unfath. Beth sy'n digwydd pan ydym yn torri'r siapiau allan ac yn eu cylchdroi? Gosodwch y siâp cyntaf fel y mae ar y daflen a chylchdroi'r siapiau eraill drwy chwarter troad bob tro. Cofnodwch eich canlyniadau.

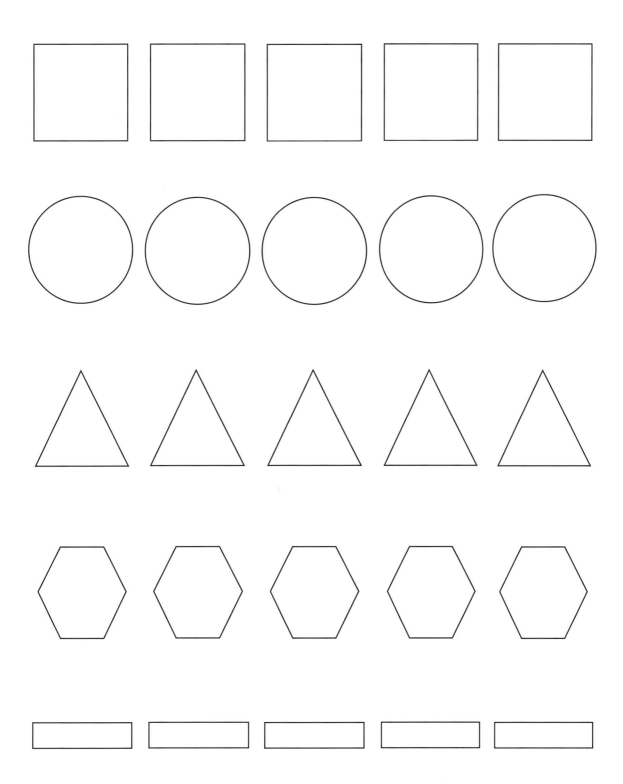

TAFLEN WAITH 3

(Cysylltiedig â Llenwi siâp 13 tudalen 10). Defnyddiwch sgwariau cm i lenwi'r siapiau. Faint ohonynt sydd eu hangen ar gyfer pob siâp? Efallai y bydd yn rhaid i chi dorri rhai sgwariau.

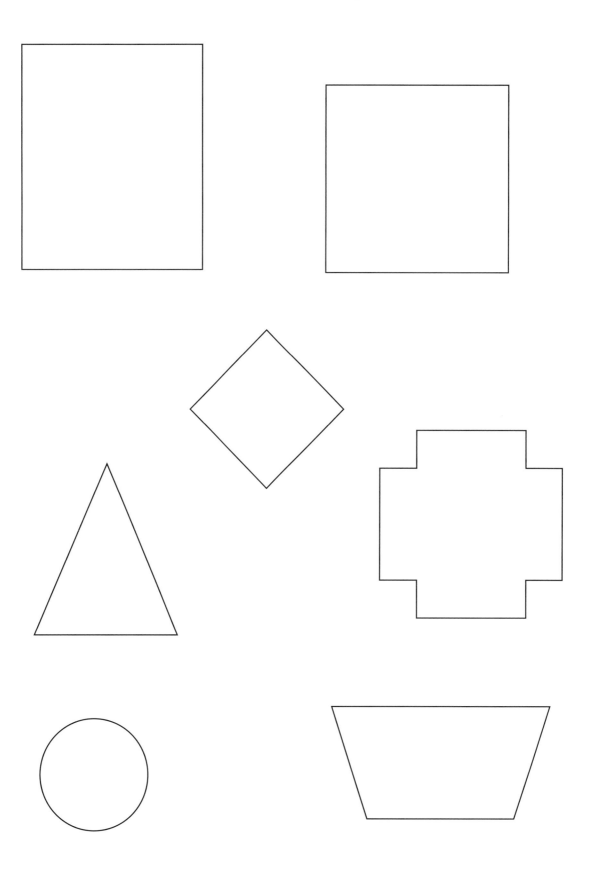

TAFLEN WAITH 4

(Cysylltiedig â Chylchau 14. tudalen 10)

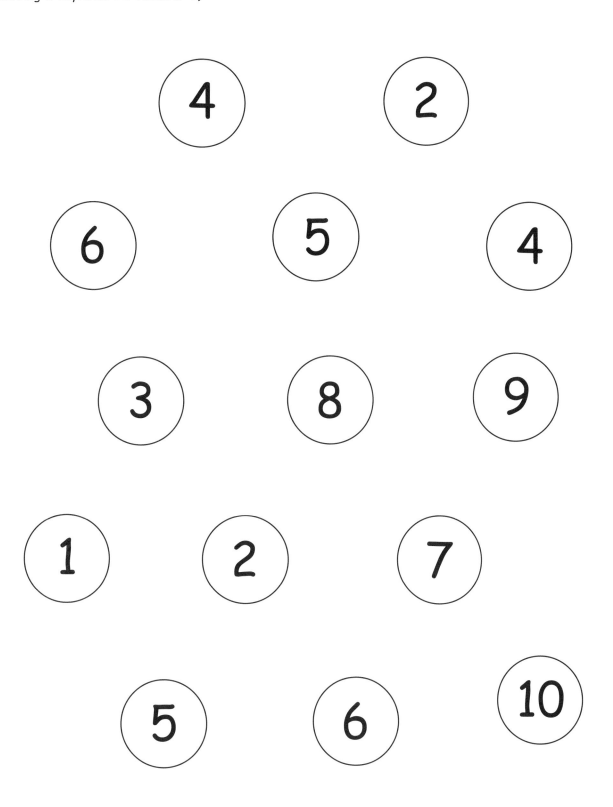

Cychwynnwch ar unrhyw gylch. Darganfyddwch lwybr i wneud _____.
Faint o rifau wnaethoch chi eu defnyddio?
Allwch chi wneud llwybr gwahanol i wneud ____?
Faint o rifau wnaethoch chi eu defnyddio y tro hwn?

1	2	3	4	5	6	7	8	9	10
11	12	13	14	15	16	17	18	19	20
21	22	23	24	25	26	27	28	29	30
31	32	33	34	35	36	37	38	39	40
41	42	43	44	45	46	47	48	49	50
51	52	53	54	55	56	57	58	59	60
61	62	63	64	65	66	67	68	69	70
71	72	73	74	75	76	77	78	79	80
81	82	83	84	85	86	87	88	89	90
91	92	93	94	95	96	97	98	99	100

DARTIAU

Amcanion

- Adio a thynnu cyflym yn y pen, ac i bwrpas, hyd at 180
- Lluosi â 2 a 3 yn y pen

Adnoddau

- Yn ddelfrydol, bwrdd dartiau a dartiau
- Copïau o'r llun o fwrdd dartiau, tudalen 18
- Copïau o'r taflenni DARTIAU ar dudalen 19

Cyflwyniad dosbarth

Defnyddiwch daflunydd tros ysgwydd neu ddelwedd o fwrdd dartiau ar fwrdd gwyn, a sefydlwch gyda'r dosbarth pa rifau sy'n cael eu sgorio ac ym mhle. Bydd rhai ohonynt yn gwybod – manteisiwch ar hyn wrth drosglwyddo'r wybodaeth i weddill y dosbarth. Rhowch gopi o'r llun ar dudalen 18 i bob disgybl.

Mae dart sy'n taro sector rhwng y cylchoedd yn sgorio'r rhif sydd wedi ei nodi wrth y sector hwnnw. Os yw'n taro'r sector y tu allan i'r cylch allanol mae'n sgorio sero. Os yw'n glanio yn y cylch allanol, mae'n sgorio dwbl y rhif a ddangosir, ac os yw'n glanio o fewn y cylch mewnol mae'n sgorio trebl. Mae'r canol yn sgorio 25 (rhan allanol) a 50 (mewnol – y bwl).

Gwnewch rywfaint o ymarfer rhifyddeg pen gyda'r dosbarth, er mwyn iddynt gael cyfle i ymgyfarwyddo â'r bwrdd ar yr un pryd, drwy bwyntio at eich delwedd o fwrdd a gofyn cwestiynau megis:
Beth sy'n cael ei sgorio yma, a beth yw'r cyfanswm? Pwyntiwch at a) dwbl 4, b) dwbl 6, c) dwbl 10, ch) trebl 5, d) trebl 8, dd) 10 a dwbl 10, e) 4 a dwbl 6.

Gweithgaredd 1

Gofynnwch i'r disgyblion weithio mewn parau. Rhowch gopi o'r CYFANSYMIAU DARTIAU i bob pâr (tudalen 19). Dylai un o bob pâr ddarllen Rhestr A, gan roi munud i'w bartner gyfrifo'r cyfanswm ym mhob cwestiwn a'i ysgrifennu. Po fwyaf y gallant eu cyfrifo yn eu pennau, gorau oll. Yna dylai'r partner arall ddarllen Rhestr B i'r partner cyntaf. Yna dylent ymuno â'r pâr sydd nesaf atynt i gadarnhau'r atebion.

Trafodaeth ddosbarth ar gyfer Gweithgaredd 2

Trafodwch reolau dartiau gyda'r dosbarth – drwy ddefnyddio 'holi ac ateb' sefydlwch y canlynol:
Fod pob chwaraewr yn dechrau ar sgôr o 301 neu 501, yna'n taflu 3 dart yn ystod pob tro ac yn tynnu'r rhifau mae'n eu sgorio o'i gyfanswm blaenorol. Y nod yw gorffen ar sero, ac mae'n rhaid i'r dart olaf daro dwbl neu'r bwl (er nad oes raid ichi ddefnyddio'r 3 dart yn ystod eich tro olaf). Yn ogystal â hyn mae'n rhaid i chi daflu dwbl i ddechrau.

Gwnewch rywfaint o rifyddeg pen gyda'r dosbarth, a gofynnwch iddynt dynnu pob dart, yn ei dro, nes cyrraedd sgôr derfynol ar gyfer y tro hwnnw, e.e.
Dechreuwch ar 301, taflwch ddwbl 10, 5, 20.
Dechreuwch ar 147, taflwch 19, 20, 1.

Gweithgaredd 2

Gofynnwch i'r disgyblion weithio mewn parau unwaith eto. Rhowch gopi o'r SGORAU DARTIAU i bob pâr (tudalen 19). Dylai un o bob pâr ddarllen rhestr C, gan roi munud i'w bartner gyfrifo'r sgorau terfynol ar gyfer pob cwestiwn drwy dynnu'r 3 dart, fesul un, o'r sgôr 'gychwynnol'. Dylent ysgrifennu'r ateb o leiaf. Po fwyaf y gallant eu cyfrifo yn eu pennau, gorau oll. Yna dylai'r ail bartner ddarllen Rhestr D i'r cyntaf.

17

Yna dylent ymuno â'r pâr sydd nesaf atynt i gadarnhau'r atebion.

Trafodaeth ddosbarth ar gyfer Gweithgaredd 3

Dywedwch wrth y dosbarth: "Erbyn hyn mae fy sgôr i wedi dod i lawr i 50. Cofiwch, mae'n rhaid i mi orffen â dwbl (neu mae'n bosibl cael y bwl). Sut allaf i orffen y gêm yn ystod fy nhro nesaf?" Dylech gael llawer o awgrymiadau, e.e. un dart yn y bwl; deg, dwbl 20; 20 dwbl 15 etc. Cofiwch, yn ystod tro terfynol gallwch ddefnyddio un, dau neu dri dart.

Gweithgaredd 3

Eglurwch i'r dosbarth eich bod chi eisiau iddynt chwilio am ffyrdd o orffen â 3 dart neu lai gan ddechrau o rai sgorau eraill. Rhowch restr iddynt, e.e.: 40, 20, 70, 100, 16, 7, 25, 38, 12, 160, 95, 39. Gofynnwch iddynt weithio mewn grwpiau o dri

neu bedwar a chyfrifo gymaint o ffyrdd ag sydd bosibl ar gyfer pob un, yn uchel wrth y grŵp, ac yna dylai gweddill y grŵp awgrymu mwy os gallant.

Gweithgaredd 4

Gofynnwch i'r disgyblion ysgrifennu'r rhifau o 1 i 60, a chofnodi gyferbyn â phob rhif, gan ddefnyddio tic neu groes, a yw'n bosibl ei sgorio ag un dart yn unig. Yn achos pob rhif gofynnwch i'r disgyblion ddweud faint o ddartiau sydd raid eu defnyddio a gofynnwch iddynt ysgrifennu sym adio'r sgorau. Er enghraifft, mae 39 yn drebl 13, mae 40 yn ddwbl 20, ond mae'n rhaid cael 2 ddart ar gyfer 41 (20x2+1 neu 19x2+3 etc).

CYFANSYMIAU DARTIAU

Rhestr A

1. Pedwar, deg, dwbl 5.

2. Dwbl tri, chwech, un deg un.

3. Un deg pedwar, deg, saith.

4. Trebl 4, saith, pump.

5. Chwech, dwbl 20, 15.

6. Naw, un deg saith, dwbl wyth.

7. Dwbl 16, pump, un deg dau.

8. Dwbl tri, dwbl saith, dwbl 13.

9. Trebl 20, un deg pump, chwech.

10. Dwbl 20, trebl 20, deg.

Rhestr B

1. Chwech, dwbl 10, pedwar.

2. Dwbl pedwar, saith, naw.

3. Un deg pump, wyth, deg.

4. Chwech, saith, trebl 5.

5. Pedwar, dwbl un deg pump, 20.

6. Un deg un, un deg chwech, dwbl 9.

7. Dwbl 19, pedwar, saith.

8. Dwbl pedwar, dwbl chwech, dwbl 14.

9. Un deg tri, trebl 8, dau ddeg.

10. Dwbl deg, trebl deg, dwbl 20.

SGORAU DARTIAU

Rhestr C

1. Dechreuwch ar 100, sgoriwch 20, 20, 8

2. Dechreuwch ar 200, sgoriwch drebl 20, 5, 1

3. Dechreuwch ar 150, sgoriwch drebl wyth, 6, 10

4. Dechreuwch ar 75, sgoriwch 20, dwbl 5, 12

5. Dechreuwch ar 87, sgoriwch 12, 12, 10

6. Dechreuwch ar 42, sgoriwch 2, 20, dwbl 10

7. Dechreuwch ar 53, sgoriwch 13, 20, 10

8. Dechreuwch ar 91, sgoriwch ddwbl 20, 11, dwbl 20

9. Dechreuwch ar 301, sgoriwch ddwbl 10, 20, 5

10. Dechreuwch ar 501, sgoriwch ddwbl 11, 20, trebl 20

Rhestr D

1. Dechreuwch ar 100, sgoriwch 10, 20, 6

2. Dechreuwch ar 200, sgoriwch 20, trebl 5, 1

3. Dechreuwch ar 150, sgoriwch drebl 20, 4, 10

4. Dechreuwch ar 75, sgoriwch 20, dwbl 6, 5

5. Dechreuwch ar 87, sgoriwch 14, 11, 10

6. Dechreuwch ar 52, sgoriwch 2, 10, dwbl 20

7. Dechreuwch ar 63, sgoriwch 13, 10, 20

8. Dechreuwch ar 71, sgoriwch ddwbl 20, 11, dwbl 10

9. Dechreuwch ar 301, sgoriwch ddwbl 11, 20, 1

10. Dechreuwch ar 501, sgoriwch ddwbl 10, 20, trebl 20

GÊM 31

Amcanion

- Adio yn y pen hyd at 31
- Trefnu gwaith a gwirio canlyniadau
- Datblygu strategaethau i ddatrys problemau

Adnoddau

- Setiau o'r pedwar âs, ac o'r rhifau 2, 3, 4, 5 a 6 o becyn o gardiau cyffredin, neu gywerth gan ddefnyddio cownteri wedi eu rhifo neu gardiau rhifau pwrpasol.

Cyflwyniad dosbarth

Eglurwch i'r dosbarth yr hyn sy'n digwydd yn y gêm:

Mae dau chwaraewr, yn eu tro, yn dewis un cerdyn o'r set ac yn ei ychwanegu at res o gardiau â'u hwynebau i fyny, ac yn nodi'r cyfanswm cronnus. Yr enillydd yw'r chwaraewr sy'n llwyddo i gael cyfanswm o union 31, neu sy'n gorfodi ei wrthwynebydd i gael mwy na hynny.

Dewiswch ddisgyblion i ddod i flaen y dosbarth a chwaraewch un neu ddwy o gêmau enghreifftiol gyda hwy. Gallech ddefnyddio Blutack i osod y cardiau ar fwrdd du neu fwrdd gwyn.

Prif weithgaredd

Rhannwch y dosbarth yn grwpiau o bedwar a gofynnwch i bob grŵp chwarae digon o gêmau fel bo pob disgybl yn cael cyfle i chware yn erbyn ei gilydd. Gofynnwch i'r disgyblion nodi pwy gychwynnodd a phwy a enillodd bob tro, a gofynnwch iddynt gofnodi canlyniadau eu grŵp mor daclus ag sydd bosibl. Gofynnwch iddynt hefyd chwilio am strategaethau sy'n sicrhau llwyddiant.

Crynodeb

Trafodwch â'r disgyblion yr hyn y gwnaethant ei ddarganfod.

Gwaith estynedig/addasiad

Rhowch gynnig ar setiau eraill o rifau a gwahanol dargedau.

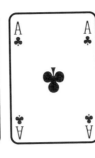

PATRYMAU AR FWRDD GWYDDBWYLL

Mae gwyddbwyll yn gêm haeddiannol boblogaidd mewn llawer o ysgolion a chartrefi ac mae gan y sgiliau o feddwl yn glir a dadansoddi sydd eu hangen er mwyn llwyddo yn y gêm lawer yn gyffredin â llinynnau strategaethau mathemategol. Ond yn ogystal â hyn, mae'r bwrdd gwyddbwyll ei hun, a symudiadau rhai o'r darnau, wedi ysgogi amryw o astudiaethau mathemategol buddiol. Rhai gweithgareddau yn unig sydd yma o'r nifer fawr a ddatblygwyd dros y canrifoedd.

Adnoddau

Yn yr holl weithgareddau bydd angen copïau o'r gridiau 8×8 ar tud. 22, a digon o bapur sgwariau lle gellir llunio gridiau llai. Bydd ar yr athro/athrawes angen grid tryloyw ar gyfer taflunydd tros ysgwydd, neu gyfarpar tebyg ar gyfer bwrdd gwyn.

1. Symudiad y Marchog

Amcanion

- Llunio ac adnabod siapiau 2-D
- Nodi cymesuredd adlewyrchiad a chymesuredd cylchdro
- Nodi cymesureddau siapiau 2-D

Gweithgaredd

Gofynnwch i'r disgyblion – sut y mae'r marchog yn cael symud? Trafodwch a dangoswch y symudiadau 1 i fyny, 2 ar draws neu 2 i fyny, 1 ar draws. Rhowch daflen o "fyrddau" gweigion i bob disgybl a gofynnwch iddynt arbrofi â chyfres fer o symudiadau marchog ar un bwrdd, un yn dilyn y llall i ffurfio llwybr caeedig. Er enghraifft, a yw

marchog yn gallu symud mewn sgwâr, neu driongl? Dylent lunio'r symudiad llinell syth rhwng canolau'r sgwâr cyntaf a'r sgwâr olaf ym mhob achos. Pan fyddant wedi rhoi cynnig ar rai cyfresi o symudiadau, gofynnwch iddynt ddod at y bwrdd du/gwyn i ddangos eu canlyniadau a'u rhannu â gweddill y dosbarth. Trafodwch unrhyw gymesuredd sydd gan y llwybrau. Dangosir rhai enghreifftiau isod.

Nawr anogwch y disgyblion i gynhyrchu eu siapiau caeedig eu hunain ac ymchwilio i'w cymesuredd. A yw hi'n bosibl gwneud hecsagon neu octagon? Siapiau sêr, croesau, diemyntau?

Crynodeb

Trefnwch sesiwn dosbarth cyfan arall i rannu a thrafod syniadau.

Gwaith estynedig

1. A ellid gosod rhai o'r siapiau gyda'i gilydd i lenwi clawr anferth heb adael bylchau? A oes rhai o'r siapiau yn brithweithio?
   Mae'r patrwm '16 symudiad' a ddangosir (isod ar y dde) yn un o bedwar siâp '16 symudiad'. Rhowch y 4 gyda'i gilydd i lunio un siâp a fydd yn brithweithio.
2. Pos adnabyddus yw: A yw'n bosibl i farchog fynd i bob sgwâr ar y bwrdd unwaith ac unwaith yn unig mewn cyfres ddi-dor o symudiadau. Gofynnwch i'r disgyblion arbrofi hyn ar "fyrddau" llai.

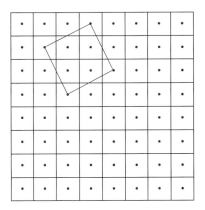
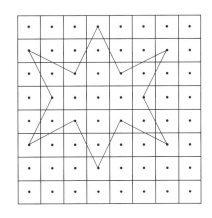
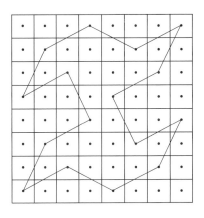

2. Breninesau Diogel

Amcanion

- Gweithio yn systematig
- Rhoi cynnig ar wahanol ddulliau

Gweithgaredd

Gofynnwch i'r disgyblion sut y gall brenhines gipio brenhines arall. Drwy drafod, sefydlwch fod angen iddi fod un ai yn yr un rhes, yn yr un golofn neu ar yr un groeslin.

Gosodwch un frenhines ar fwrdd enghreifftiol ar y taflunydd. Gofynnwch i'r disgyblion ddweud wrthych ym mhle y gallwch osod brenhines arall gerllaw. Gofynnwch ym mhle y gallwch roi trydedd brenhines. Anogwch hwy i awgrymu tynnu llinellau llorweddol, fertigol a chroeslinol i ddileu unrhyw sgwariau peryglus.

Gofynnwch i'r disgyblion weithio ar eu pen eu hunain er mwyn darganfod sawl brenhines y gellir ei gosod ar y bwrdd yn ddiogel. Rhaid iddynt ystyried gwahanol fannau cychwyn ar gyfer y frenhines gyntaf. Efallai mai'r syniad gorau fyddai eu hannog i arbrofi â byrddau llai yn gyntaf, e.e. 4 sgwâr wrth 4 sgwâr, 5 wrth 5, etc i weld sut y mae'r patrwm yn datblygu.

Crynodeb

Trafodwch eu darganfyddiadau. Sicrhewch eu bod yn deall y cysylltiad rhwng gosod y breninesau a symudiad y marchog.

3. Sawl sgwâr sydd ar fwrdd gwyddbwyll?

Amcanion

- Gweithio yn systematig
- Rhoi cynnig ar wahanol ddulliau
- Adnabod a disgrifio patrymau rhif

Gweithgaredd

Trafodwch y cwestiwn a chynorthwywch y disgyblion i ddechrau deall ei ystyr.
Gofynnwch iddynt weithio mewn parau i'w ddatrys. Trafodwch y canlynidau gyda'r dosbarth.

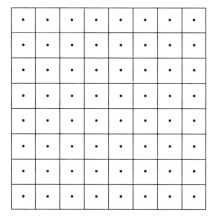
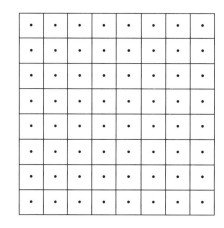
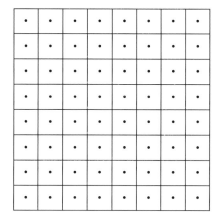

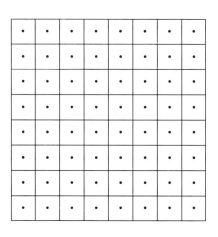
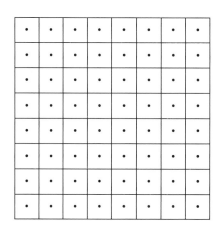
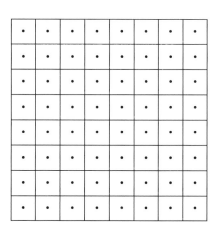

22

MOCHYN

Mae hon yn gêm glasurol sydd wedi cael ei chwarae ers blynyddoedd lawer, ac mae yma gryn botensial i ysgogi amrediad o fathemateg. Ar y lefel fwyaf syml mae'r gêm yn gyfle da i ymarfer rhifyddeg pen; gall hefyd arwain at gasglu a thrin data a hefyd (yn achos Lefel A) gellir ei dadansoddi yn nhermau tebygolrwydd.

Gêm i 2 neu fwy o chwaraewyr yw hon – mae pedwar yn fwyafrif synhwyrol.

Amcanion

- Adio rhifau yn y pen, yn gywir ac yn gyflym
- Datblygu strategaethau ar gyfer datrys problemau
- Trafod gwaith ac egluro ffyrdd o feddwl
- Casglu a chofnodi data arwahanol
- Llunio a dehongli diagramau amlder

Adnoddau

- dis cyffredin wedi ei rifo: 1, 2, 3, 4, 5, 6
- papur a phensil i nodi'r sgorau (tynnwch linellau ar y papur i gael un golofn i bob chwaraewr)

Cyflwyniad dosbarth

Y ffordd hawsaf o gyflwyno'r gêm yw drwy chwarae gêm enghreifftiol gyda grŵp bychan o ddisgyblion ym mlaen y dosbarth a chofnodi'r sgôr ar y bwrdd du/gwyn neu'r taflunydd.

Mae pob chwaraewr, yn ei dro, yn taflu'r dis gymaint o weithiau ag y mae'n dymuno, ac yn cofnodi'r rhif sy'n cael ei daflu. Ar ôl penderfynu ei fod wedi gorffen mae'n adio ei gyfanswm at unrhyw sgôr flaenorol ac yn ei chofnodi fel prif gyfanswm yn ei golofn ar y daflen sgorio. Os yw'r chwaraewr yn taflu 1 ar unrhyw adeg yn ystod ei dro, mae ei dro yn dod i ben ac mae'n colli'r holl farciau a sgoriodd hyd yma yn ystod y tro hwnnw. Y chwaraewr cyntaf i gyrraedd 100 neu fwy sy'n ennill.

Prif weithgaredd

Gofynnwch i'r disgyblion roi cynnig ar chwarae'r gêm ychydig o weithiau mewn grwpiau o 3 neu 4. Yna trafodwch sut y gallant wella eu strategaethau.

Trafodwch pa waith ymchwil y gallent ei wneud i helpu, e.e. taflu'r dis nifer fawr o weithiau er mwyn darganfod y nifer 'cyfartalog' o weithiau y gellir taflu'r dis cyn i 1 ymddangos. Y ffordd orau o wneud hyn fyddai drwy grynhoi canlyniadau pob grŵp yn y dosbarth.

Gofynnwch i'r disgyblion gasglu, crynhoi, dadansoddi ac arddangos y data.

Yng ngoleuni'r canlyniad, gofynnwch iddynt drafod y cwestiynau:

Sawl tafliad sy'n synhwyrol yn ystod pob tro?

A oes sgôr arbennig y dylech orffen eich tro ar ôl ei chyrraedd?

Gofynnwch i'r disgyblion chwarae'r gêm eto, gan ddefnyddio'u syniadau.

Gofynnwch iddynt: Sut y mae'r atebion i'r cwestiynau hyn yn newid os ydym yn newid y rhif "tyngedfennol" o 1 i dyweder 6 neu 3?

Crynodeb

Gofynnwch i'r grwpiau roi sylwadau ar eu darganfyddiadau.

Cysylltiadau

Ceir fersiwn 'fasnachol' o'r gêm hon – "Pass the Pigs" – y gellir cael gafael arni'n hawdd ac mae'n gêm hynod o ysgogol, yn arbennig ar gyfer yr amrediad oedran Iau.

NIM

Gêm hynafol iawn yw Nim ar gyfer dau chwaraewr. Credir fod y gêm yn dod yn wreiddiol o China, ond fe'i chwaraeir drwy'r y byd i gyd â gwahanol gyfarpar ond yr un yw'r rheolau sylfaenol.

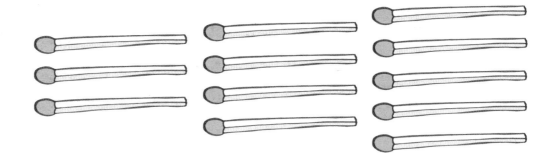

Amcanion

- Datblygu strategaethau ar gyfer datrys problemau
- Cyflwyno canlyniadau mewn ffordd eglur a threfnus
- Dilyn cadwyn o symudiadau posibl a chadw'r posibiliadau eraill yn eu pennau wrth iddynt ddatblygu eu dull o ymresymu

Adnoddau

- setiau o fatsys wedi eu defnyddio, neu setiau o ddarnau arian unfath

Cyflwyniad dosbarth

Gan ddefnyddio silwetau ar daflunydd tros ysgwydd, neu luniau syml, dangoswch y 3 rhes o fatsys neu ddarnau arian i'r dosbarth. Eglurwch y rheolau:
- Mae pob un o'r ddau chwaraewr, yn ei dro, yn cymryd un fatsen neu fwy o unrhyw res.
- Mae'r chwaraewr sy'n cymryd y fatsen olaf yn colli.

Nawr gofynnwch i nifer o ddisgyblion unigol, yn eu tro, chwarae'r gêm yn eich erbyn chi. Anogwch weddill y dosbarth i roi sylwadau a thrafod y symudiadau.

Prif weithgaredd

Unwaith y bydd hi'n amlwg fod y syniadau wedi eu sefydlu, gofynnwch i'r dosbarth weithio fesul grwpiau o bedwar. Ym mhob grŵp o bedwar dylai pob chwaraewr chwarae yn erbyn pob un o'r lleill a chofnodi'r canlyniadau mewn tabl. (Os dymunwch, gallech drefnu fod enillwyr y grwpiau yn chwarae yn erbyn ei gilydd a darganfod pencampwr y

dosbarth ar y diwedd, ond efallai y byddai'n well gennych fynd yn syth at y dadansoddiad). Gofynnwch i'r disgyblion chwilio am strategaethau. A oes rhai symudiadau cychwynnol sy'n well nag eraill? A oes rhai sefyllfaoedd y dylid eu hosgoi tua diwedd y gêm, e.e. sefyllfaoedd lle mae'r un sy'n chwarae nesaf yn sicr o golli? Allwch chi sylwi ar sefyllfaoedd o'r fath, a hynny ymhell cyn iddynt ddigwydd?

Crynodeb

Trafodwch strategaethau â'r dosbarth ac anogwch hwy i ddatblygu syniadau. Gofynnwch iddynt chwarae'r symudiadau eraill posibl yn eu pennau, o sefyllfaoedd sy'n bellach fyth oddi wrth ddiwedd y gêm a chreu casgliad o "sefyllfaoedd chwarae nesaf a cholli" (h.y. gan gymryd mai fod y chwaraewr arall yn chwarae'n berffaith!).
Enghreifftiau da o hyn yw:
Rhesi o 2 a 2; 3 a 3, 1, 2 a 3; 1, 4 a 5

Syniadau am waith estynedig ar gyfer gwersi pellach

Gellir defnyddio unrhyw nifer o fatsys ac unrhyw nifer o resi.
Darganfuwyd dadansoddiad syml yn nhermau nodiant cyfrif deuaidd tua 1900: ysgrifennwch y nifer deuaidd o fatsys ym mhob rhes, y naill o dan y llall. Adiwch y golofn unedau, colofn 2 a cholofn 4, ysgrifennwch yr atebion ar ffurf ddegol. Os yw'r holl ddigidau yn eilrifol, y sefyllfa yw "chwarae nesaf a cholli". Os nad ydynt, dangosir pa symudiad y dylech ei wneud drwy gyfrifo pa symudiad fydd yn gadael colofnau eilrifol i'ch gwrthwynebydd.

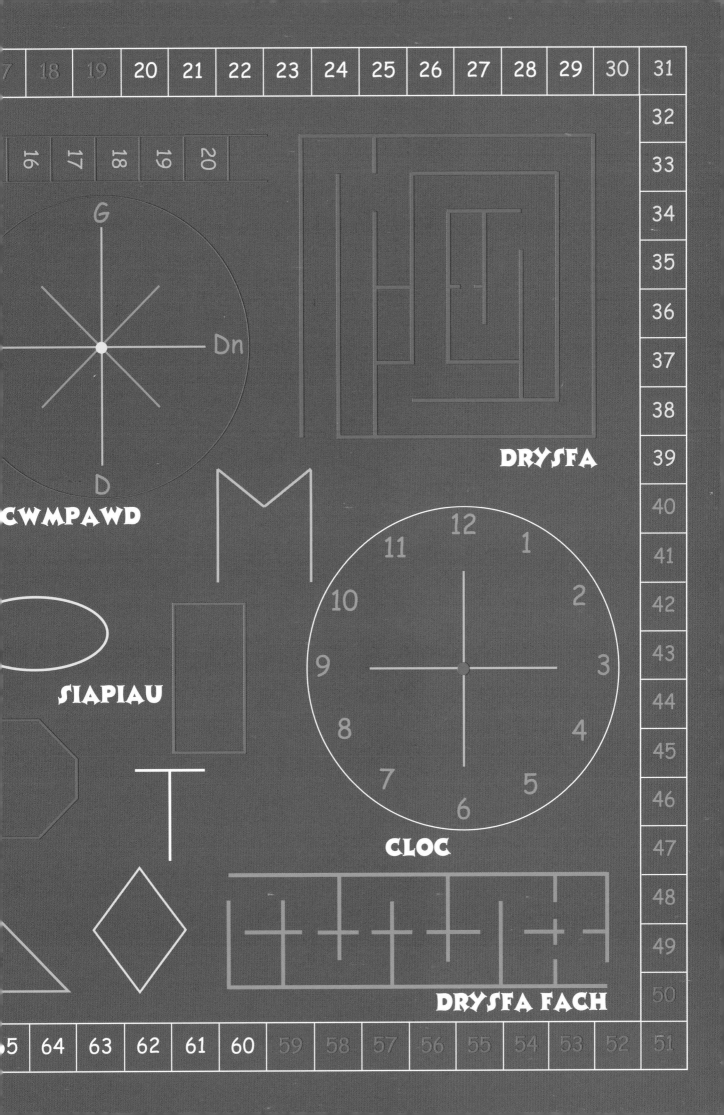

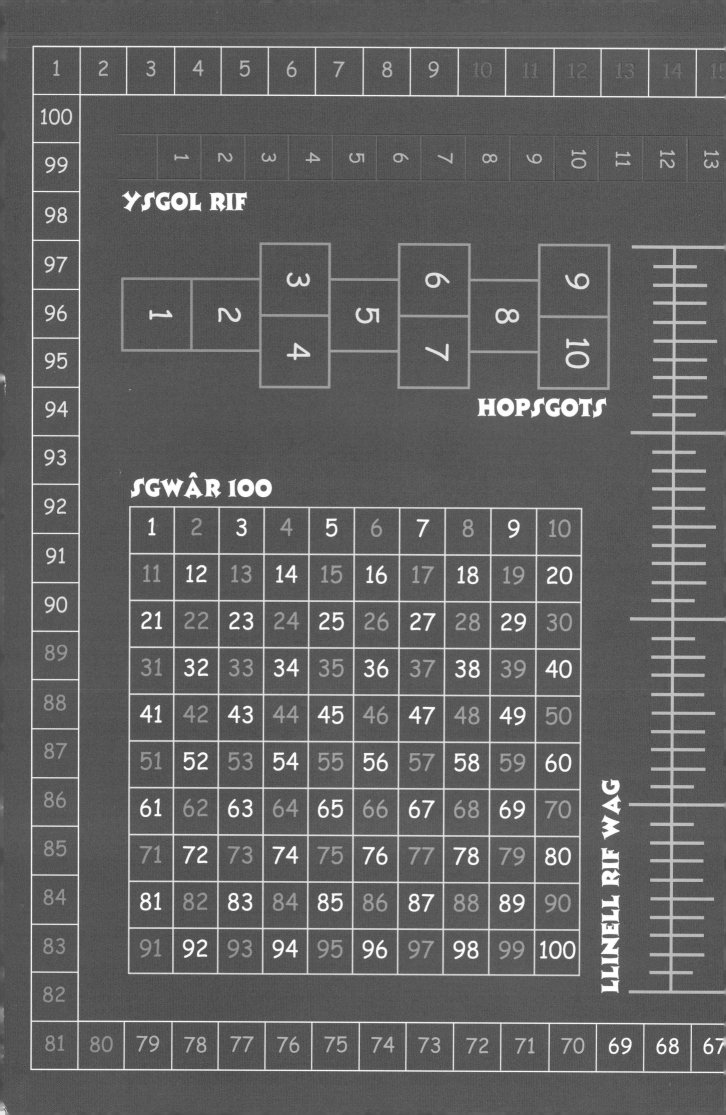

FORMULA 1

L E G E N D S

FORMULA 1
LEGENDS

DOUG NYE

MAGNA
BOOKS

Published by Magna Books
Magna Road, Wigston
Leicester LE18 4ZH

Produced by Bison Books Ltd, Kimbolton House
117A Fulham Road, London SW3 6RL

ISBN 1-85422-650-9

Printed in Slovenia

PAGE 1: Sheer class; the most successful Formula 1 driver of all
time has been French ace Alain Prost, here *en route* to winning
his fourth World Championship title – in the 1993 Williams-
Renault at Monaco.

PAGES 2-3: The most exciting driver of his time: fearless,
indefatiguable French-Canadian Gilles Villeneuve's exploits for
Ferrari 1977-1982 made "27" the most charismatic race number in
Formula 1 . . .

THESE PAGES: Victory! Five times World Champion Juan Manuel
Fangio savours the moment at Silverstone as he exits Woodcote
Corner in his works Lancia-Ferrari D50A to win the 1956 British
Grand Prix.

CONTENTS

INTRODUCTION

This book is about people – special people, men of extra-ordinary physical and sensory capability, the finest racing drivers the modern world has known ... Today race driving success tends to be equated with World Championship-winning status, but don't be taken in too much by the importance of that formal title. While the best drivers in the best cars will always take the lion's share of success, there are many examples of the finest driver around being denied that elusive World Championship by simple, tricky, luck.

None can deny that Stirling Moss was absolutely the standard-setting racing driver of his day from Fangio's retirement in 1958 until his own career-ending accident at Goodwood in 1962. He never won the World title yet every other racing driver at that time judged his own performance by how close he could get to Stirling's lap times. "Mossy" was the man by whom his rivals judged themselves – the standard-setter of his time.

Subsequently, the same became true of the great Swede Ronnie Peterson during the later 1970s. Not always equipped with the fastest car, his was still the first name others would seek when anxiously scanning the practice lap times. Ronnie at that time had become what American sportsmen call "The Man". ... Hence, when considering those who might be described as "Formula 1 Legends" we must consider a number of factors and not rely solely on the record books, for these can sometimes be misleading.

So much for the "Legend" status, now what of Formula 1 itself? Modern Formula 1 motor racing traces its thoroughbred heritage all the long way back to the summer of 1906 when the *Automobile Club de France* organized its maiden "Grand Prix" motor race. This great new event offered open entry to any manufacturer and driver interested in fielding cars complying with certain technical regulations – these regulations became known as "the Grand Prix Formula."

From that earliest beginning, Grand Prix racing evolved into the major league of international motor sport – the purest, and the best. Up until the outbreak of World War II in 1939, drivers competed in Grand Prix races for what was then known as the European Championship title – forerunner of the modern Drivers' World Championship.

After hostilities had ceased in 1945, the governing body of the sport – the Paris-based *Federation Internationale de l'Automobile* (FIA) – published a set of regulations for 1948-51 which established classes initially known as Formula A and Formula B. The former sat squarely on top of the pile to govern the great classic national *Grande Epreuve* or Grand Prix races, while the less powerful Formula B provided a trainee class just beneath it for minor and local GPs. The letters identifying each Formula rapidly gave way to figures, and the more familiar "Formula 1" and "Formula 2" soon became normal useage.

Until 1949 there was no formal Championship structure governing postwar top-level motor racing, but everybody knew which races were the major ones. These were the old, established Grand Prix races which continued to be run like clockwork, year after year. The French, Swiss, Belgian, Italian and latterly the British GPs formed a top-level series which no major team would readily ignore.

From 1950, the FIA recognized this fact and announced its new Drivers' World Championship series, which grouped the major races into a formal series, with points awarded upon results and a Champion to be declared at the end of the year. The Formula 1 Drivers' World Championship had thus been founded and it is still thriving today, well into the 1990s.

There has been only a brief break in Formula 1's primacy – during the seasons of 1951-52 – when the number of competitive F1 race entries contracted so catastrophically that the FIA transferred World Championship status instead to Formula 2. From 1954 a new set of Formula 1 regulations took effect, and the class has remained supreme ever since.

World Champion Drivers 1950-1993

1950	Dr. Giuseppe Farina *Italy* – Alfa Romeo.
1951	Juan Manuel Fangio *Argentina* – Alfa Romeo.
1952	Alberto Ascari *Italy* – Ferrari.
1953	Alberto Ascari – Ferrari.
1954	Juan Manuel Fangio – Maserati & Mercedes-Benz.
1955	Juan Manuel Fangio – Mercedes-Benz.
1956	Juan Manuel Fangio – Lancia-Ferrari.
1957	Juan Manuel Fangio – Maserati.
1958	Mike Hawthorn *England* – Ferrari.
1959	Jack Brabham *Australia* – Cooper-Climax.
1960	Jack Brabham – Cooper-Climax.
1961	Phil Hill *U.S.A.* – Ferrari.
1962	Graham Hill *England* – BRM.
1963	Jim Clark *Scotland* – Lotus-Climax.
1964	John Surtees *England* – Ferrari.
1965	Jim Clark – Lotus-Climax.
1966	Jack Brabham – Brabham-Repco.
1967	Denny Hulme *New Zealand* – Brabham-Repco.
1968	Graham Hill – Lotus-Cosworth Ford.
1969	Jackie Stewart *Scotland* – Matra-Cosworth Ford.
1970	Jochen Rindt *Austria* – Lotus-Cosworth Ford.
1971	Jackie Stewart – Tyrrell-Cosworth Ford.
1972	Emerson Fittipaldi *Brazil* – Lotus-Cosworth Ford.
1973	Jackie Stewart – Tyrrell-Cosworth Ford.
1974	Emerson Fittipaldi – McLaren-Cosworth Ford.
1975	Niki Lauda *Austria* – Ferrari.
1976	James Hunt *England* – McLaren-Cosworth Ford.
1977	Niki Lauda – Ferrari.
1978	Mario Andretti *U.S.A.* – Lotus-Cosworth Ford.
1979	Jody Scheckter *South Africa* – Ferrari.
1980	Alan Jones *Australia* – Williams-Cosworth Ford.
1981	Nelson Piquet *Brazil* – Brabham-Cosworth Ford.
1982	Keke Rosberg *Finland* – Williams-Cosworth Ford.
1983	Nelson Piquet – Brabham-BMW.
1984	Niki Lauda – McLaren-TAG Turbo.
1985	Alain Prost *France* – McLaren-TAG Turbo.
1986	Alain Prost – McLaren-TAG Turbo.
1987	Nelson Piquet – Williams-Honda.
1988	Ayrton Senna *Brazil* – McLaren-Honda.
1989	Alain Prost – McLaren-Honda.
1990	Ayrton Senna – McLaren-Honda.
1991	Ayrton Senna – McLaren-Honda.
1992	Nigel Mansell *England* – Williams-Renault.
1993	Alain Prost – Williams-Renault.

LEFT: Ronnie Peterson, the great Swedish racing driver of the 1970s, was that rare animal in Formula 1 – a universally respected and popular driver without a single enemy. For simple speed around a circuit he was also the standard setter of his time . . . but tragedy awaited him.

RIGHT: A prime candidate for the title "The Best There Has Ever Been" – "Flying Scotsman" Jimmy Clark winning the 1962 British Grand Prix at Aintree in his works Lotus 25, the trend-setting new monocoque-chassised car which was delicate, elegant, and Fast!

JEAN-PIERRE WIMILLE

1908-1949

This great French driver is barely remembered today, simply because he lost his life before the modern Drivers' World Championship was launched, in 1950. But if there had been such a competition in 1946, 1947 or 1948 it seems quite probable that this urbane Parisian would have taken that hat-trick of World titles. Yes, in the immediate postwar years, Jean-Pierre Wimille was as good as that, and as dominant – indisputably the standard-setting driver of his time.

Wimille had been born in 1908, and made his Grand Prix racing debut as early as 1930, in his own Bugatti, learning his craft in the French GP at Pau. He was keen, and wealthy, and he became a valued Bugatti customer – sharing works cars in 1931 before shifting his allegiance to Alfa Romeo in 1932, when he won the minor Lorraine GP in France.

He returned to Bugatti in 1934 as a works driver handling their fabulous – but already outmoded – Type 59 3.3-liter supercharged cars with their famous "piano-wire" wheels. He won the Algiers GP and continued to campaign Bugattis in following seasons although the Alsace factory was falling ever farther behind contemporary German GP car technology.

Wimille always gave his best, but his machinery was incapable of winning. The French authorities – aggrieved by continual German success – then ran their 1936 Grand Prix for sportscars and Wimille and his friend Raymond Sommer shared the victorious Type 57G Bugatti "Tank." He won again in the Marne and Comminges GPs, and at Deauville, and drove a special 4.7-liter Bugatti *monoplace* racing car home second in the Vanderbilt Cup race on Long Island, U.S.A.

In 1937 Wimille won the Le Mans 24-Hours with Robert Benoist, sharing a Bugatti "Tank," and in 1939 he won there again, this time with Pierre Veyron. But as Bugatti's racing activities contracted, Wimille also began to race a private Alfa Romeo in the period leading up to the war.

During the war he served with the French Air Force and then the Resistance, and in 1945 he won the first postwar feature race, in the Bois de Boulogne, Paris, driving Bugatti's 4.7-liter *Monoplace*. Anxious to show friendship to a recent enemy, the Italian Alfa Romeo company then offered him a drive in its *Tipo* 158 GP car team for 1946. He shone. Driving to team orders, he came third in Geneva and second in Turin, but significantly he set the fastest race lap both times.

In 1947 he was free to drive as he wished, and he won the European and Swiss GPs for Alfa Romeo. In 1948 he dominated the French, Italian, and Monza GPs while also appearing occasionally in the little Paris-built 1100cc Simca-Gordinis.

That winter found him in Argentina, driving these little cars in President Peron's *Temporada* race series. But in January 1949, while practising for a race in Buenos Aires' Palermo Park, he spun his little French-blue car: it hit a tree, and Europe's finest racing driver was fatally injured.

ABOVE: Speed with style – Bugatti factory team leader Jean-Pierre Wimille finger tips his works Type 59 past the pits and into another rapid lap around the Monte Carlo street circuit in the 1934 Monaco Grand Prix. He would establish himself as the man to beat driving for Alfa Romeo after the war.

RIGHT: Having time both to acknowledge the photographer and to glance across the infield to check upon his pursuers, Wimille excites the crowd at Thillois Corner, Reims-Gueux, during the 1948 French Grand Prix.

JUAN MANUEL FANGIO

1911-

No other racing driver has yet succeeded in challenging the phenomenal career record of this Argentine doyen of all Grand Prix legends – Fangio, the *Maestro*. This tubby, balding master with the impassive and relaxed mien which was more Nordic than Latin, was the Argentinian-born son of Italian immigrants who did not even begin racing in Europe until he was already 37, then drove at premier level until he was 47 – whereupon he quietly, gracefully, retired.

During his career, for Alfa Romeo, Maserati, Mercedes-Benz, and Ferrari, Fangio – he pronounced it "Fang-hio" – accumulated 24 Grand Prix victories in an era in which they were far rarer currency than they are today. More to the point, Fangio secured an unequaled five Drivers' World Championship titles, four of them consecutively from 1954-57.

His roots were in humble Balcarce, a small dusty town in Buenos Aires province, Argentina. An accomplished soccer player in his teens, Fangio became a garage mechanic and learned the art of throttle control on unsealed local roads which were powdery dust in summer and axle-deep mousse-like mud in winter.

He began track racing in assorted makeshift specials before World War II, then embarked on super-long distance *Carretera Turismo* racing, winning the *Gran Premio Nacionale del Norte* in 1949, over 6000 miles of public trackway from Buenos Aires to Lima, Peru – and back! He learned patience, mechanical sympathy, how to read the road ahead, and the mysterious arts of pace and tempo. He learned far more than most of his European rivals would ever be equipped even to imagine.

In the summer of 1948 the national Argentine Auto Club despatched him on a fact-finding trip to Europe and in 1949 – encouraged by visiting European racing drivers – the ACA deployed a full team in Europe, with Fangio driving a new Maserati 4CLT and a little Gordini. He won races at Pau, San Remo, Perpignan, Marseilles, Monza and Albi, and instantly became the sensation of the season.

The works Alfa Romeo team offered him a drive for 1950. Thrilled to accept he challenged veteran Italian Nino Farina for the FIA's inaugural World Championship title and won the Monaco, Belgian and French GPs. He won three more in 1951, and the second postwar World Championship title was his.

LEFT: Full throttle noise – the great Juan Fangio unleashing all the enormous horsepower of his supercharged works Alfa Romeo *Alfetta* in vain pursuit of his compatriot Froilan Gonzalez's unsupercharged V12 Ferrari in the 1951 British Grand Prix at Silverstone. The supercharged cars were fiendishly fast but fuel thirsty, and so they started races heavy and had to refuel more times than their economical unsupercharged rivals. But Fangio still took his first World title.

RIGHT: *Maestro* – nearing the peak of his fabulous career, Fangio drove for Mercedes-Benz in 1954-55 and became World Champion both seasons.

Because Alfa Romeo then retired from F1, Fangio agreed to drive BRM and Maserati in 1952 but he broke his neck in an accident at Monza, having driven there overnight from Paris after racing in Ulster the previous day. He was out for the rest of the year.

For 1953 he led Maserati's World Championship F2 charge against Ascari and Ferrari, and won the Italian GP. He began the 1954 season for Maserati, winning in Argentina and Belgium, but had signed to transfer to Mercedes-Benz once the great German team was ready. When they emerged, he immediately won them the French, German, Swiss and Italian GPs.

Through 1955 Fangio showed Moss how in a totally dominant Mercedes season, but after the team's withdrawal at the end of 1955 Fangio encountered difficult times. His most influential supporter had been Argentine President Juan Peron. Now Peron had been toppled and the new regime was investigating Fangio's private and business affairs, suspecting malfeasance. Fangio knew his hands were clean, but with his assets frozen he needed secure income. He had planned to retire together with Mercedes-Benz, but now Mr Ferrari offered him terms for 1956 and he accepted.

The latest Lancia-Ferrari D50 cars were tricky, and Fangio and Ferrari did not cohabit comfortably, but "The Old Man," as his young rivals called Fangio, still won his third consecutive World Championship title, his fourth overall.

For 1957 he returned to his first love after Alfa Romeo – Maserati, Ferrari's great rival across the street in Modena. Driving the immortal works "Lightweight" Maserati 250Fs he won the Argentine, Monaco, French and German GPs. That final victory on the majestic Nürburgring passed into motor racing history as one of the most tremendous driving displays of all time. After losing the lead to the Lancia-Ferraris of Hawthorn and Collins in a botched mid-race refuelling stop, Fangio ripped the lap record to shreds, passed them both, and almost literally "ate them alive," to clinch his fifth and final World Championship crown.

He was now 46 years old, but he drove again, briefly, in Argentina at the start of 1958. He also tried to qualify an appalling private car for Indianapolis, and then ran a revised Maserati 250F into fourth place in the French GP at Reims. He retired immediately thereafter, withdrawing to Argentina to run his extensive Mercedes-Benz distributorship and other interests in Balcarce and Buenos Aires.

He would continue to travel the world as revered as royalty at any motor racing venue, fit and crisp, firm and shrewd – there's only one J. M. Fangio – arguably the greatest racing driver the world has ever seen.

LEFT: What the well-dressed World Champion was wearing in 1957 – Fangio fastening his Herbert Johnson cork, fiber and canvas crash helmet with peak-supported plastic vizor. He has a standby pair of goggles round his neck, and lightweight sports shirt and trousers. The jacket will be discarded before the race.

ABOVE: Fangio didn't start racing seriously in Europe until he was 39. He became revered by this youthful rivals, and could beat them all! Here at Reims in 1956 team-mates Peter Collins (hidden), Eugenio Castellotti, and Olivier Gendebien hang on every word.

RIGHT: Swansong – As reigning World Champion for the fifth time, Fangio drove the famous "Lightweight" Maserati 250F in this, his last Argentine GP, Buenos Aires, 1958.

ALBERTO ASCARI

1918-1955

During the early 1950s, the most famous name combination in motor racing became "Ascari, Ferrari." Burly, friendly Alberto Ascari proved himself the fastest racing driver of his day in the latest Formula 2 Ferrari 500 Grand Prix cars.

Through the racing seasons of 1952-53, Ascari did not merely feature among the top four or five stars contesting the Drivers' World Championship. He simply sat there on top of the pile and dared all others to knock him off it. They failed. Just consider his 1952 record in his 4-cylinder Ferrari model '500s . . .

Seven European Grands Prix comprised that year's mainstream Championship series. Ascari started in six, and won them all: the Belgian, French, British, German, Dutch and Italian. In 1953 he added five more World Championship-qualifying Grand Prix wins, in the Argentine, Dutch, Belgian, British, German and Swiss GPs. As if that was not enough, he also drove his works Ferrari in minor F2 events of which he won six in 1952 and two more in 1953.

Motor racing in those days was not the highly-sponsored media-rich sport-cum-business we see today, but don't make the mistake of believing it must have been uncommercialized. Far from it. Many major manufacturers were involved in racing to "Win on Sunday, Sell on Monday." Race success for a motor manufacturer sold road-going production cars.

In the case of such a specialist manufacturer as Ferrari, race success achieved an extra aim – earning valuable bonuses from commercial suppliers. For every race that Ascari won, he earned himself, and Ferrari, cash from oil, fuel, spark plug, bearings, damper and tire manufacturers, in addition to starting fees and prize money from the race promoters themselves.

Racing at such a level, with such a skilful driver, paid big money for the time. It was good business, and Ascari was very much aware of this, as his late father, Antonio Ascari, had been Alfa Romeo's number one racing driver during the 1920s.

Alberto himself, born on July 13, 1918, had been barely six years old when his famous father was killed

LEFT: Alberto Ascari – World Champion 1952-53 – was burly, muscular and blindingly fast on circuit, but an assured, relaxed, charming and friendly man off it. Here he is in the 2-liter Formula 2 Ferrari 500. He started the 1953 British Grand Prix here from poll position, led from start to finish, broke the lap record *and* beat Fangio's under-developed Maserati by a clear minute.

ABOVE RIGHT: Ascari leading the dominant Ferrari 500 team into turn one of the 1953 Dutch Grand Prix – Luigi Villoresi, Nino Farina, Juan Fangio (Maserati) and Mike Hawthorn in the fourth works Ferrari follow on. Ascari won again – of course . . .

while leading the French Grand Prix at Montlhéry. Antonio had been pressing just too hard. Alberto developed into the same kind of driver – but perhaps with more intelligence.

He began racing motor-cycles before combining with a friend, the Marchese Rangoni, to commission former Alfa Romeo team chief Enzo Ferrari to build a brace of special sportscars for the 1940 Mille Miglia 1000-Mile race at Brescia. These two cars – known simply as the "815s" – went well, before retirement, and Ascari then honed his skills in 1500cc "Formula 2" Maseratis before World War II engulfed his country.

When the hostilities were over Ascari resumed racing teamed with Luigi Villoresi in the Maserati *Voiturettes*. They accumulated an entire string of victories – Ascari learning rapidly on the heels of Villoresi, his older friend and mentor.

They became virtually inseparable, driving for Maserati (1946-48) and then Ferrari (1949-53). When the dominant factory Alfa Romeo team took a sabbatical for 1949, Ascari dominated Formula 1 in Ferrari's latest supercharged V12 cars. Alfa burst back in 1950 and the scene was set for battle royal with Ferrari. Ascari fought a series of terrific top-class duels with Fangio and Farina – the Alfa drivers always winning on technical superiority.

Using new 4.5-liter unsupercharged cars against the 1.5-liter supercharged *Alfettas*, Ascari then led Ferrari to destroy Alfa's domination in 1951. His team-mate Gonzalez won the British GP, and Ascari took the German and Italian. Ascari and Villoresi – the inseparables – joined the new Lancia team for 1954-55. The new Lancia D50 became the only Formula 1 design to seriously threaten Mercedes-Benz at that time, and Ascari found himself fighting Fangio and Stirling Moss in their German cars virtually alone.

In the 1955 Monaco GP he had just taken the lead as the Mercedes of Moss and Fangio had failed, when he lost control at the harborside chicane. His Lancia burst through a straw-bale barrier and plunged into the deep harbor. A great cheer went up from the crowd as Ascari's bright-blue helmet broke surface, and the muscular Italian struck out strongly to be dragged aboard a waiting safety boat. He had escaped with a broken nose, shock, and a soaking.

Four days later, testing reactions to his accident in a sports Ferrari at Monza, in Italy, the double World Champion's luck ran out. He inexplicably lost control on the back leg of the course, his Ferrari overturned, and Italy's finest postwar driver died. He had been a great, good and popular man. He was mourned by all who had known him.

STIRLING MOSS

1929-

Few modern racing drivers would – or have the chance to – drive as many different racing cars as the great Stirling Moss once customarily handled during each season of his dazzling career. Whereas today an F1 driver will seldom contemplate driving anything other than his F1 cars, the stars of old such as Moss simply raced anything. Stirling always claimed that he raced to live, and earnings from his racing had to be maximized, so he drove just about everything, everywhere.

His range included Formula 1, Formula 2 and even 500cc motorcycle-engined Formula 3 cars, the entire spectrum of sports-racing machinery, saloons large and small, Grand Touring cars, track-racers, even highly specialized record breakers.

Stirling's father Alfred was a prosperous dentist who had raced at Brooklands and even Indianapolis between the wars, while his mother Aileen had been a successful lady trials driver. Stirling was raised as a highly competitive young man, first show jumping on ponies, then sprinting a BMW 328 sports in 1947, aged 17. Into 1948 the Moss family had acquired a 500cc F3 Cooper and Stirling would continue to race – and win – in that class until as late as 1954.

In 1950 George Abecassis of HWM recognized the boy's startling talent and took him on a full European road-racing season in Formula 2. He also drove Jaguar sportscars and rapidly made his name as Britain's leading new driver. He was intensely patriotic and longed for a British Grand Prix car capable of taking on the then-dominant Italians. He tried the BRM V16 but found the program a shambles. While he struggled with British cars through 1952-53, his young rival Mike Hawthorn joined Ferrari, and won the French GP.

Ultimately Alfred Moss and other backers bought Stirling a Maserati 250F for the new 2½-liter F1 class of 1954, and in that he shone – earning full factory backing and being invited to join Fangio in the mighty Mercedes-Benz work team for 1955.

There he learned at the great Argentine's feet, following in his wheel-tracks but winning the British GP at Aintree. While he always deferred to Fangio in Formula 1, Stirling had his measure in sports-racing cars, and he won the legendary Mille Miglia, the RAC TT and the Targa Florio in his Mercedes-Benz 300SLRs.

After the German team's withdrawal, Moss returned to Maserati for 1956, winning the Monaco and Italian GPs then drove Tony Vandervell's new Vanwalls

ABOVE: Stirling Moss on his way to scoring his maiden *Grande Epreuve* victory in the 1955 British Grand Prix at Aintree driving the factory Mercedes-Benz W196.

LEFT: Learning curve – Stirling had first to prove himself in this private Maserati 250F during 1954 before Mercedes snapped him up for '55. Here Moss leads Mike Hawthorn's Ferrari 625 at Silverstone.

RIGHT: Moment to savour – Moss stands for "The Queen" after winning the 1956 Italian Grand Prix at Monza as *numero uno* for Maserati.

through 1957-58. Sharing with Tony Brooks he won the British GP at Aintree, then won at Pescara and Monza, thrashing the Italians on their home ground – victories he truly savoured.

Into 1958, Moss fought hard for the World title with Mike Hawthorn of Ferrari. Mike won it by one point, but had won only one GP to Stirling's three. Moss had been driving Rob Walker's private Coopers in minor F1 and F2 races, and once Vanwall withdrew for 1959 he drove the latest 2½-liter rear-engined Coopers and a front-engined BRM in World Championship rounds.

In 1960 Walker bought new rear-engined Lotus 18s for his star. Stirling crashed badly in practice at Spa and broke his back, but he bounced back in time to win the Portuguese and U.S. GPs. Through 1961 there was no chance of beating the latest V6 Ferraris to World title honors, but on the two most demanding GP circuits – Monaco and Nürburgring – Stirling beat the Ferrari drivers in Walker's obsolescent 4-cylinder Lotus 18.

Into 1962 there was talk of Walker running a private Ferrari for "Mr. Motor Racing," but the new British Climax V8 engine showed enormous promise, and then Stirling suffered an inexplicable accident at Goodwood, which left him in a coma for weeks and ended his frontline career. He never won the World title, but he came second every year from 1955 to 1958. It took him three years or more to recover fully, but he skilfully turned his ex-superstar status into a new career, developed widespread business interests and returned to racing "just for fun" in the historic and saloon car classes. And just beneath the skin, the 18-year-old Stirling Moss – genuine motor racing enthusiast – has survived throughout.

LEFT: When you're hot, you're hot. By 1960-61 Moss was unquestionably the world's greatest racing driver. His margin of superiority was so great he was attracted by the idea of racing as an underdog, with a private team versus the factories. Rob Walker fielded this Scots-blue Lotus 18 for him, and Stirling triumphed in Formula 1 with it through 1960 (when the car was current) and 1961 – by which time it had become obsolescent.

RIGHT: Simply the best – Britain's "Mr. Motor Racing" throughout the 1950s – but the Goodwood safety bank lay in wait for him on Easter Monday, 1962 . . .

MIKE HAWTHORN

1929-1959

Four truly great English racing drivers made their names during the 1950s – Tony Brooks, Peter Collins, Stirling Moss and John Michael Hawthorn.

Mike's father, Leslie, had raced motorcycles before the war and ran the TT Garage business in Farnham, Surrey, race-preparing customer's cars. Leslie encouraged Mike to begin racing, first with a prewar Riley sports, and then, for 1952, an old family friend – Bob Chase – bought a new Formula 2 Cooper-Bristol for Leslie to prepare, and Mike to drive.

The new team made its sensational debut at the Easter meeting at Goodwood in 1952, when tall, burly, blond, young Mike won three races. They then pursued a Grand Prix campaign which saw Mike shine brightly – fourth behind the all-conquering Ferraris in both the Belgian and Dutch GPs.

At Boreham Mike's tiny 2-liter Cooper led works driver Villoresi's mighty 4½-liter Ferrari in pouring rain. Enzo Ferrari was impressed and gave the young Englishman a works team place for '53. He was the first Briton to gain a drive with a major Continental GP team since Dick Seaman of Mercedes-Benz before the war, and he made his mark by beating Fangio's Maserati in a classic confrontation in the French GP at Reims.

In early 1954 Hawthorn was burned in a collision at Syracuse, Sicily, and then suffered personal trauma as his father Leslie was killed in a road accident. A number of close friends lost their lives in race and road accidents with cars and motorcycles, and the carefree boy rapidly matured into a darker, deeper character. Despite these problems, Mike still won the Spanish GP.

The need to run his TT Garage business kept him in England more through 1955-56. So he drove for the British teams Vanwall, and then BRM, but neither was successful. As team leader of the Jaguar sportscar squad he did better, but his victory with Ivor Bueb at Le Mans in 1955 was marred by involvement in the tragic "Levegh" Mercedes-Benz accident in which over 80 spectators and the French driver were all killed.

Hounded by the press, Mike became even more intense and hunted. A natural extrovert, his high jinks often assumed near-hooligan proportions. He was also dogged by a chronic kidney ailment. Sometimes, if he was feeling fit, he was a ferociously effective racing driver. At other times, parchment white, he seemed merely a makeweight.

But Ferrari invited him back for 1957-58, teaming him with his knock-about sparring partner, Peter Collins in one of the strongest driver teams around, but in 1958 after a string of second places and points-scoring fastest race laps, and a magnificent second victory in the French GP at Reims, Mike saw Collins killed just ahead of him at Nürburgring during the German GP.

Hawthorn decided then to retire at season's end, and second place in the Moroccan GP finale earned him Britain's first-ever Drivers' World Championship title, by just one point from Stirling Moss.

He seemed liberated by retirement, but fate left him no time to enjoy the business future he planned. One January morning in 1959 – barely 12 weeks after his title win and subsequent retirement – Mike Hawthorn crashed his 3.4 Jaguar saloon into a tree beside the Guildford Bypass and was killed.

LEFT: Overnight star – Mike Hawthorn in the unpainted Bob Chase-owned Cooper-Bristol prepared by his father Leslie, in which he made his name with such shattering impact on Easter Monday, 1952, at Goodwood.

ABOVE: Grand Prix winner – Hawthorn slithering his Ferrari *Squalo* around the Pedralbes boulevard circuit at Barcelona during the 1954 Spanish Grand Prix.

RIGHT: Fun lover – on his good days, when he felt bright and well, Hawthorn was a tremendous joker, a beer-drinking, womanising *bon viveur*. His green windcheater and bow-tie became his racing trademarks – the French press admired the stylish tie and nicknamed him *Papillon* (butterfly) after it.

WOLFGANG VON TRIPS

1928-1961

"Taffy" von Trips was a German Count. A highly-educated, civilized and cosmopolitan character, he was fluent in several languages, charming, friendly, and fun-loving. He was also a naturally talented athlete and sportsman, a highly competitive man, and a very fast driver indeed. He was born in 1928, began driving competitively in his private Porsche, and aspired to a works supported Porsche drive in the 1954 Mille Miglia round-Italy road race. Sharing with Hampel he won the 1300cc GT class and gained the taste for more.

He ran a Porsche at Le Mans in 1955 and was then invited to join the factory Mercedes-Benz team – the dominant racing power of the time – as a cadet sportscar driver. He handled their potent 300SLR factory cars well in the Swedish GP and at the Ulster TT, and when Mercedes withdrew from racing for the 1956 season he returned to his old friends at Porsche, winning the 1500cc class at Le Mans in a car shared with Richard von Frankenberg.

By that time "Taffy" – and his habitual Tyrolean hat – was a well-known figure around the motor racing circuits of Europe and late that season he was invited to join the Ferrari team, driving in his first Grand Prix for them in Argentina in 1957.

He was a fine open road racer – arguably better on the great point-to-point courses than on the closed circuits – and he finished second for Ferrari in the mighty Mille Miglia. He drove Porsches in the European Mountain Championship and Ferrari Formula 1 and 2 cars through 1958-59. He won the Mountain Championship title for Porsche in 1958, the Sebring 12-Hours sportscar classic – with Jo Bonnier – in 1959, and gave Porsche their Formula 2 single-seater debut that same year.

In 1960 he remained with Ferrari despite Porsche's offers of a Formula 2 drive for them, and in fact he beat the Porsches in the latest rear-engined F2 Ferrari on their home course at Solitude, just outside Stuttgart – Germany's best driver was beating the home team, on Italy's behalf.

By this time von Trips was a fixture at Ferrari and in their legendary "Sharknose" cars for the new 1.5-liter Formula 1 class of 1961, he fought a season-long battle for the World Championship with his American teammate Phil Hill. "Taffy" won the Dutch and British GPs and was leading the Championship chase by one point going into the decider – the Italian GP at Monza, on Ferrari's home soil.

However, on the second race lap there, he collided with young Jimmy Clark's works Lotus. His Ferrari careered out of control, ran up a trackside bank into the crowd, and somersaulted back, to crash upside down on to the roadway. "Taffy" – and 14 spectators – had been killed in the worst motor racing accident of the 1960s. It was a ghastly fate for one of the most popular men in motor racing.

LEFT: A cool head, deft touch, and a racer's determination all shone through as "Taffy" von Trips dominated the 1961 British Grand Prix here at a rainswept Aintree circuit, Liverpool. His car is the legendary "Sharknose" 1½-liter V6 Ferrari.

RIGHT: "Black Jack" – the great practician – Jack Brabham from Australia winning the 1960 French Grand Prix at Reims-Gueux in his "Lowline" rear-engined Cooper-Climax.

JACK BRABHAM

1926-

"Black Jack" – so named after his perpetually dark-shaven and "nut-brown Australian" looks – is regarded by many who know as having been the smartest operator ever to have won the Drivers' World Championship. The fact that he won the title three times – latterly with his own cars operated by his own team – is evidence of just how bright Jack could be.

A taciturn, self-contained, silent man, Jack worked by choice with men of similar mien. His business partner and race car designer Ron Tauranac was another man of few words, and many of the fine Australian mechanics they employed were similarly silent. There was a story that the Brabham Racing Organization's men one day interrupted a troupe of Trappist monks to complain about their incessant chatter. Not talkers, perhaps, but doers – and didn't "Black Jack" always do the job so well. . . .

Jack Brabham grew up in Hurstville outside Sydney, New South Wales, only son of a greengrocer. He learned practical mechanics working on his father's trucks before taking a garage job and then serving with the Royal Australian Air Force late in the Pacific war. He was attracted first to midget-car dirt track racing, then bought a Cooper-Bristol for which he arranged commercial sponsorship from RedeX which brought a clash with the conservative Australian racing authority.

Estranged from Australian racing he shone in the New Zealand international series of 1954-55 and was urged to race in Britain and Europe by Dean Delamont, a visiting luminary from the British RAC. He appeared in England that spring, bought a Cooper-Alta – which was a mistake – and then for 1956 an ex-BRM team Maserati 250F – a worse mistake. But he had also forged a firm friendship with John Cooper of the Cooper Car Company, and as a good practical mechanic he built and raced his own Cooper cars, using the factory's facilities in Surbiton, England.

His first special rear-engined Cooper-Bristol had given him his F1 debut in the 1955 British GP at Ain-

LEFT: Reigning World Champion Jack Brabham with New Zealander Bruce McLaren at the 1960 NZ Grand Prix in Auckland. Both were as gifted mechanically as they were as racing drivers – both would found marques.

RIGHT: The first Grand Prix driver ever to win a Formula 1 race in a car bearing his own name – Jack Brabham does the trick the Repco Brabham BT19 in the 1966 French Grand Prix at Reims-Gueux.

BELOW: Dry, taciturn "Blackie" also had a sense of humor. Nettled by press comments upon his 40th birthday Jack walked out onto the 1966 Dutch GP grid like this – and won.

tree, and in 1956 he showed real pace in Cooper sports and F2 cars. In 1957 private entrant Rob Walker financed a hybrid F1 Cooper-Climax in which Jack took sixth place at Monaco. As Cooper found its feet in Formula 1 that season, so did its team drivers.

Through 1958 Brabham simply learned the ropes of Grand Prix racing and with full 2½-liter Climax engines freshly available for 1959 he won the Monaco and British GPs and clinched the World Championship in that year's final round, at Sebring, Florida.

Jack then masterminded the design of a new "Low-line" Cooper-Climax F1 car for 1960 and drove it in a spectacular succession of five consecutive GP victories to become the first driver since Ascari to secure back-to-back Drivers' titles.

Into the new 1½-liter Formula of 1961-65 Cooper's technical star waned, and Jack left to start his own Grand Prix team with Tauranac, giving their F1 proto-type BT3 car its debut in the 1962 German GP. With Dan Gurney as team driver Jack decided to play a secondary driving role through 1963-65 yet remained a formidable contender, particularly in lucrative Formula 2 racing in which he never stopped winning.

For 1966 and the new 3-liter Formula, Jack appreciated that the major F1 teams would take too complicated an approach so he and Tauranac aimed instead for practical simplicity.

They adopted Australian-built Repco V8 engines based upon humble American Oldsmobile F85 production blocks, and while slaughtering all F2 opposition in his Honda-powered "Brabham" cars, Jack then became the first driver ever to win a *Grande Epreuve* in a Formula 1 car bearing his own name when he won the French GP at Reims that July. Successive victories followed in the British, Dutch and German GPs – and Jack walked out to the start of the Dutch event (on his 40th birthday) wearing a long false beard and leaning upon a walking stick! For the third time Jack Brabham was World Champion, and this time he was World Champion Constructor too.

Through 1967 his Repco Brabhams continued winning, new team-mate Denny Hulme taking the title from Jack at season's end after "Blackie" had won the French and Canadian GPs.

In 1968 the Repco link was overwhelmed by European opposition – and in 1969 Jack ran Jacky Ickx as his number one, using Cosworth-Ford power in his latest BT26A cars. In 1970 he won the South African GP, and led both the Monaco and British GPs into the final lap before – respectively – being robbed by a mild crash on the very last corner and running out of fuel . . .

Such class in his final season was typical of the man, and he retired gracefully, and with tremendous honor – returning to his native Australia to run his ever-expanding business network with typically quiet tenacity and shrewdness.

In the 1985 New Year's Honours list, Sir Jack Brabham became motor racing's first postwar knight. Such honor was never better deserved.

PHIL HILL

1927-

Intense, serious, some said highly strung (which would always set Phil gibbering "I only get highly-strung when journalists tell me I'm highly-strung . . . "), the first American ever to win the FIA Drivers' World Championship title was born in 1927 in Miami, Florida, and raised in Santa Monica, California, son of the city postmaster.

Phil became a lifelong lover of fine motorcars, fine craftsmanship and fine music. Regarded very much as the "thinking man's World Champion," he was also a highly articulate and skilled racing driver, a lover of the fastest race circuits, and perhaps, above all, a tremendous sportscar pilot.

He studied at Jaguar's Coventry factory in England during a comprehensive motor industry apprenticeship and began his racing career in an MG TC, winning his first race in 1950, at Pebble Beach on California's Pacific coast. By 1952 he had aspired to racing Ferraris for their private owners. He shared one with his great friend Richie Ginther to finish sixth in the mind-bogglingly dangerous point-to-point *Carrera Pan-Americana* multi-stage classic through Mexico. Hill's exploits with Ferrari cars in the U.S.A. were beginning to earn him factory interest from Italy, and in 1954 he shared an Italian OSCA sportscar at Le Mans. In that year's *Carrera* Phil's fearlessly fast driving on the Mexican public roads brought him and passenger Ginther second place overall; and in 1955 Phil and Carroll Shelby shared a *Monza* Ferrari to finish second to a works-backed D-Type Jaguar in the Sebring 12-hours – America's most important "enduro."

American Ferrari importer Luigi Chinetti arranged a works Ferrari sportscar drive for him in the 1956 Argentine 1000 km race, in which Hill and the patrician Belgian Olivier Gendebien finished second. An invitation followed to join Ferrari in Europe.

He progressed rapidly, but was consistently denied an F1 drive as Enzo Ferrari saw him as a sportscar specialist. Phil actually had to take a private Maserati F1 drive to convince Ferrari's management he could show similar pace in open-wheelers!

He won the Le Mans 24-Hours classic in 1958, 1961 and 1962, teamed every time with Gendebien, and in 1960 he had won it again, teamed with Paul Frere. He won the Sebring 12-Hours with Peter Collins in 1958 and with Gendebien in 1959 and 1961.

Ferrari finally gave him his regular-team F1 debut in 1958, and Mike Hawthorn paid special tribute to Phil's role in the last two Championship-deciding GPs of that season, in Italy and Morocco, which won Mike the title. In 1960 Phil became the first American since Jimmy Murphy in 1921 to win a *Grande Epreuve* in Europe with victory in the Italian GP at Monza.

The World Championship season of 1961 with the Ferrari "Sharknose" cars then became a straight fight between team-mates Phil Hill and "Taffy" von Trips. Phil won the Belgian GP, finished second in the Dutch and British, third in the Monaco and German events, and then won the Italian GP at Monza to clinch the Drivers' title – only to learn that von Trips had been killed in his second-lap accident. Phil was appalled and stunned. He stayed with Ferrari for 1962 – a mistake. He moved to the new ATS team for the 1963 F1 season – another mistake, then Cooper for 1964 – a third . . .

After three dreadful seasons of disappointment he retired from Formula 1 but found a new lease of life with Jim Hall's all-American Chaparral sportscar team. On 30 July 1967, he and English co-driver Mike Spence won the BOAC 6-Hours race at Brands Hatch in their bewinged Chaparral-Chevrolet 2F Coupe, whereupon Phil Hill – once described as "Hamlet in a Helmet" – bowed out at the top, as a respected elder statesman of motor racing, with style.

GRAHAM HILL

1929-1975

Tall, moustachioed, a man with an often wicked sense of humor, Graham Hill was a Londoner. Born in 1929, through sheer determination he made himself into one of the world's top-four racing drivers.

A motor-cycle accident as a young man had left him with a permanent limp, but he fought his way into motor racing via a series of associated jobs – including mechanic to old-car dealer Danny Margulies, and storeman at Lotus Engineering's tiny original Hornsey factory. As early as 1953 he had paid £1 for four brief laps round the Brands Hatch racetrack in an elderly 500cc Formula 3 car.

He talked himself into a series of early races in other people's cars before being entrusted with drives by his employer at Lotus, Colin Chapman, from 1957. In the 1958 May meeting at Silverstone, Graham drove a single-seater F2 Lotus with oversized engine – Team Lotus's first-ever Formula 1 entry.

He then pursued a full F1 program with Lotus during 1958-59 but the fragile cars estranged him from Chap-

man and they parted at the end of that second season, with Graham moving to BRM. In their latest rear-engined 2.5-liter F1 cars he made his mark by starting last on the grid in the 1960 British GP and passing everybody to lead until within sight of the finish, when his brakes faded and he spun into an earth bank.

When the new 1.5-liter Formula 1 took effect for 1961-65, BRM developed a V8 engine and a lovely, lightweight, good-handling P578 car to match. Graham played a crucial role in the development not only of the

LEFT: Hard trier – America's first World Champion Driver, Phil Hill, hustling his "Sharknose" Ferrari around the Monte Carlo streets in the 1962 Monaco Grand Prix.

ABOVE RIGHT: Graham Hill won the World title twice – in 1962 and 1968 – here in 1969 he's in typically dour pre-race mood in his Lotus 49B.

RIGHT: The most British of British racing drivers, Graham had made his name – and won his first World title – with British Racing Motors, driving BRM cars from 1960-1966.

car's engineering but also the structure of the team which ran it.

Their efforts blossomed in 1962. Graham won his first F1 race, and the Dutch, German and Italian GPs. Into the final round in South Africa the World titles lay between Hill and BRM, Clark and Lotus. The Lotus broke, the BRM won, and Hill – ex-storeman, ex-mechanic – had become World Champion Driver.

BRM and Graham were runners-up in the respective Drivers' and Constructors' Championships for the next three seasons, 1963-65, using the P578 and its monocoque replacement, the P261. Throughout, his stature grew through continuing success in Ferrari, Porsche, Jaguar and Aston Martin sportscars. He also appeared in F2, and saloon cars, and McLaren sports-racers. He was the consummate professional, earning his keep in any decent drive he might be offered.

After winning the world's richest race – the Indianapolis 500 speedway classic – in a Mecom *Red Ball* Lola in 1966, Graham finally left BRM's F1 team at the end of that year, joining Jim Clark back at Lotus with Ford paying the bills to create a Formula 1 "dream team." With the new Cosworth-Ford DFV engine in Lotus 49 cars, the duo set the pace that season – only mechanical unreliability denying them the World title.

Clark was plainly faster, but in April 1968 he was killed and Graham towered above genuine grief and dismay by promptly scoring two consecutive GP wins to pick Team Lotus off the floor. By winning the Mexican GP at the season's end he secured his second World Championship title.

In 1969 he scored the last of his 14 Grand Prix wins – at Monaco, his fifth win in the principality – but in the U.S. GP that season he crashed horribly and smashed both legs. In 1970 he drove a private Lotus 49 for Rob Walker's little team, then led Brabham through 1971-72, winning the minor Silverstone race as his last F1 success while also driving for the French Matra team.

In 1973 he founded his own Formula 1 team with a Shadow chassis, and in 1974 campaigned customer Lolas. After failing to qualify at Monaco in 1975, Graham then announced his retirement from driving – too long after having passed his best.

Nevertheless, Hill's driving achievements were impressive. Indeed, he was the first driver ever to have won the Formula 1 World title, the Indy 500, and the Le Mans 24-Hours endurance classic.

Determined to stay within F1, he had his own Hill F1 cars designed and built, but on November 29, 1975, piloting his own twin-engined aircraft home from a test session at Ricard in the south of France, he attempted to land at Elstree Aerodrome in dense fog, and crashed at Arkley golf course, North London, during the approach. He died instantly, as did promising young driver Tony Brise and four other team members – a shattering blow to the entire motor racing world.

Graham had made himself not only into a fine racing driver, but also into one of the first Formula 1 multimedia stars. He was a single-minded, and hard man, but all his finest characteristics were inherited by his son Damon – the Grand Prix-winning novice Williams-Renault driver of 1993.

JIM CLARK

1936-1968

This quiet, rather shy and introspective sheep farmer from the Scottish borders is recalled by modern motor racing enthusiasts as much for his extraordinarily admirable character as for his record-shattering achievements on circuit. From Stirling Moss's career-ending crash at Goodwood early in 1962 until his death at Hockenheim, Germany, on April 7, 1968, Jim Clark was absolutely the standard-setter of his time. He won two World Championship titles – in 1963 and 1965 – and came within an ace of making that record four in a row, in 1962 and 1964. He raised Juan Fangio's record of 24 Grand Prix victories to 25 by victory in the 1968 South African GP, and that mark survived until 1973 when compatriot Jackie Stewart finally overturned it.

LEFT: Graham Hill launched his own Formula 1 team in 1973 with an Embassy cigarettes-liveried Shadow, followed by Lolas, as shown here, in 1974. But he would not win here at Monaco a sixth time . . .

ABOVE RIGHT: Scottish Border farmer-cum-gentleman racing driver, double-World Champion, standard setter of his time – Jimmy Clark.

RIGHT: The most mild mannered of men off track, Jim Clark could be a tiger upon it. After his own car failed in the 1963 Aintree "200" Jimmy took over his team-mate's Lotus 25. Here – even before mechanic Ted Woodley is clear of his path, Clark has the clutch engaged, the rear wheels spinning, and his eyes fixed upon the first corner. Ted survived, unscathed . . .

ABOVE: Clark at the office, settled into his figure-hugging Lotus 25 with red-leather rimmed steering wheel, peakless Bell helmet tailored to accept the strap of those carefully-taped one-piece goggles, and thin flame-retardant "Dunlop" racing overalls . . . what the early-'60s racing driver was wearing. The breast pocket badge is that of the British Racing Drivers' Club.

LEFT: A rare GP in which victory always eluded Clark – Monaco. He led repeatedly but his Lotuses always faltered . . .

RIGHT: His second World Championship title in three years just secured, Clark is with Graham Hill (2nd) and Dan Gurney (3rd) on the podium after winning the 1965 German Grand Prix at Nürburgring.

Jimmy's story is inextricably entwined with that of Team Lotus and of Colin Chapman, for he only ever drove Lotus Formula 1 cars in competition and also drove their cars in Indianapolis, Formula 2, Formula Junior, sports and even GT and saloon car classes. He was absolutely a Lotus man, through and through in a sport not noted for such marque loyalty.

Colin Chapman described Clark quite simply in these terms: "He was the finest man I ever knew. As a driver he was a complete genius . . . And, do you know, I doubt if he ever realized it." – such was Jim Clark's instinctive modesty.

His competition career began in a Sunbeam-Talbot 90 saloon in 1956, and developed through club races in his friend Ian Scott-Watson's Porsche 356. The Border Reivers racing team ran a D-Type Jaguar for him in 1958, and for 1959 he campaigned a faster Lister-Jaguar, and a Lotus Elite.

Jim made his single-seater debut in a Gemini Formula Junior car at Brands Hatch, 1959, and was invited to join the 1960 Lotus FJ works team. His GP debut followed in Holland, where he ran fourth before his car failed. He scored his maiden Championship points in the Belgian GP at Spa, and into 1961 became the hottest young property in Formula 1 with some searing performances in his works F1 Lotus 21s.

Ending that season, Chapman gave Jimmy No. 1 status within the team, and after a stunningly success-ful South African F1 tour, he emerged in 1962 with Climax V8 power in the latest Lotus 24 and monocoque Type 25 chassis and won the Belgian, British and United States GPs, plus a sequence of non-Championship F1 races.

He was denied the World title only by an engine oil leak in the deciding South African GP at East London, but in 1963 he won a record seven GPs plus numerous minor events and the World crown was his. In his Indy 500 debut, he also finished second to stand the Speedway establishment upon its ear. Through 1964 Jimmy then led the Championship chase into the final lap, of the final race, at Mexico City, only for his Climax V8 engine to expire again.

For 1965 Clark confirmed his pre-eminence – none could match him in the latest Lotuses – but the Formula change to 3-liter engines for 1966 left Lotus without competitive power. Still Jimmy fought an underdog role through that season and in 1967 was joined by Graham Hill in the new Lotus-Cosworth 49 V8 cars and they set the pace everywhere as Clark won four more Grands Prix.

Then 1968 was here, Jimmy broke Fangio's career record at Kyalami, but in April he had a tire blow out on his works Gold Leaf Team Lotus Type 48 F2 car at Hockenheim in Germany, the car smashed into a stout sapling broadside on, full in the cockpit, and broke in two. The impact was unsurviveable.

DAN GURNEY

1931-

Tall, friendly, taciturn, Daniel Sexton Gurney was the son of an American opera singer – he had a smile which radiated all the ideals of clean-cut all-American youth and he was a tremendously talented racing driver – highly-rated by his rival Jimmy Clark.

Dan made his name driving other people's Ferrari sportscars in U.S. West Coast racing, and in 1958 American Ferrari importer Chinetti took him to Le Mans as a North American Racing Team driver. Enzo Ferrari was impressed by Chinetti's recommendation, and after a test-drive Dan joined the works F1 and sports-racing teams for 1959. In 1960 he moved to BRM, then to Porsche for 1961, ever-improving along the way while also racing with great success in sports and Formula 2 cars. By 1962 Porsche had perfected an air-cooled flat-8 cylinder Formula 1 car with which Dan was able to win the French GP at Rouen and the non-Championship Solitude GP just outside Stuttgart in Porsche's own backyard.

Jack Brabham invited him to lead his F1 team through 1963-65 and the Californian was repeatedly deprived of further victories by misfortune until fate smiled – again at Rouen – in the 1964 French GP, and at Mexico at the end of 1964.

For the new 3-liter Formula 1 class introduced in 1966, Dan founded his own AAR teams – Anglo-American Racers Ltd. based in England for Formula 1 and All-American Racers Inc. based in Santa Ana, California, for Indycar competition. Their cars were named "Eagle" after the American national symbol but despite showing enormous promise, and winning the 1967 Belgian GP, the Eagle F1 program fizzled out in mid-1968, Dan reverting to a semi-works McLaren ride. He concentrated upon his USAC and Indianapolis programs through 1969, made a brief reappearance in F1 and CanAm with McLaren in 1970, but the deaths of Jimmy Clark, Bruce McLaren and Piers Courage hurt him deeply – and this deep thinking, affable man retired from race driving soon after.

He continued to run his Eagle company in America, with success varying from immense and dominant, to minimal and near-moribund, but he is still around racing into the 1990s with his Toyota sportscar team – Dan Gurney, the finest road-racing driver the U.S. ever exported to Europe, bar none.

LEFT: No racing driver ever flew higher than Jim Clark at his best. Here at Nürburgring during practice for the 1967 German Grand Prix Jimmy demonstrates this, in the literal sense, in the latest Cosworth-Ford DFV V8-powered Lotus 49.

RIGHT: Dan Gurney was another rightly respected and popular great racing driver of the 1960s, and one Clark admired. For the new 3-liter Formula of 1966 Dan founded his own marque, Eagle, and in 1967 built one of the best-looking F1 cars of all time – his Eagle-Weslake V12 seen here at Monaco's *Tabac* corner.

JOHN SURTEES

1934-

When Englishman John Surtees came to motor racing in 1960, he had already accumulated seven world titles on two wheels, riding most notably for the great Italian MV-Agusta company. He liked working with Italians. He loved their terrific heart and soul. John Surtees loved Italy and the wildly enthusiastic Italian *tifosi* simply loved him. They christened him *"Il Grande John"* – "John the Great" – which British journalists miscribed into "Big John" and so "Big John" he became, despite his average height and athletic build.

After 1959 test drives for Vanwall and Aston Martin, John drove his first race on four wheels at Goodwood, in March 1960, in a humble Cooper-BMC Formula Junior entered by Ken Tyrrell's quasi-works team.

He had bought his own 1.5-liter F2 Cooper-Climax and after showing tremendous speed in it at an early-season Oulton Park race, Colin Chapman of Team Lotus offered an immediate F1 ride at the May non-Championship Silverstone meeting. John shone brilliantly. He drove for the team again whenever motorcycle commitments permitted, and shone again in the British GP at Silverstone. He then led the Portuguese GP, looking set to win until oil smothered his foot pedals; he overshot a braking point and spun off.

For 1961 John drove Reg Parnell's private team Coopers, still learning his new craft, but those cars were never natural winners and as he pressed ever harder to compensate he earned a "hairy" reputation. Established racing drivers felt uneasy in close formation with him: he was too often a "spinner."

Through 1962 he matured immensely, building what was virtually his own Bowmaker-Lola team, using new Lola chassis and the latest Coventry Climax V8 engines. He won a minor F1 race and finished second in both the British and German GPs.

Ferrari then drew him back to Italy for 1963. *Il Grande John* would stay there until mid-1966. He enabled Ferrari to close the yawning technology gap which had opened between them and their British rivals since 1960, for he was an accomplished practical engineer, and was fast becoming one of the world's top four racing drivers. Under his leadership Ferrari retrieved competitiveness, and he won the 1963 German GP, while also leading their fabulously successful sportscar team.

John maintained the pace in 1964 and wins at Nurburgring – again – and Monza (the Italian *tifosi* went MAD!!) plus second places in Holland, the U.S.A. and Mexico – made him the only man yet to win World Championship titles on both two wheels and four.

Ferrari faltered through 1965 due to internal team politics which persisted into 1966. Enzo Ferrari himself disliked Surtees running his own sportscar team using Lola chassis.

John hurt himself badly in a Lola crash in Canada ending 1965, and his fitness to race early in 1966 raised great question marks in Italy, to which he responded typically upon his return by winning brilliantly in the Monza 1000 km sportscar classic.

A new 3-liter Formula 1 class took effect that season, and Ferrari seemed best-prepared for it. John scored a brilliant win in appalling conditions at the superfast Belgian GP, but festering political differences with Ferrari's team management exploded at Le Mans that June, and abruptly, his Ferrari career was over.

In 1966 he reappeared in the works F1 Cooper-

LEFT: Crucial event – John Surtees (Ferrari 158 number "7") lined-up for the start of the 1964 Austrian Grand Prix on Zeltweg aerodrome alongside his Italian team-mate Lorenzo Bandini (Ferrari 156). John's car will break; Bandini will win, denying Surtees' rivals crucial Championship points.

BELOW: Multiple motorcycle World Champion John Surtees comparing notes with Ferrari chief engineer Mauro Forghieri *en route* to their 1964 motor racing World title success.

Maseratis, proved himself still a front-runner, and developed these hefty cars into potential race winners, finally winning the Mexican GP that year.

Mindful of Japanese prowess in motor cycle engineering, he then signed to lead Honda in F1 for 1967-68. He gave them victory in the Italian GP at Monza. Again an Italian crowd chanted his name – how they adored him. But Honda withdrew at the end of 1968, and John then spent an unhappy season with BRM in 1969 while developing his own Team Surtees organization through Formula 5000 racing. Never a man to delegate, Sutees did *everything* within the team.

He launched his own F1 project for 1970, running an ex-works McLaren until his prototype TS7-Cosworth Ford F1 car was ready. He served as team chief, design director, and No. 1 driver through 1971, and then effectively retired from driving duties, competing in just one final GP – at Monza, of course – in September 1972.

Team Surtees continued to contest the World Championship until 1978 when John finally bowed out. He has since maintained close ties with the British motor and motor-cycle trades, and the historic two- and four-wheeled sporting worlds. He is a hugely respected figure in both his native country, and of course in Italy – *Il Grande John* indeed.

DENNY HULME

1936-1992

"Denny the Bear" was a rugged, taciturn New Zealander. Friends claimed he wasn't born, he was hewn out of solid rock! His father Clive Hulme had won the Victoria Cross at Anzio in World War II, and much of the same undemonstrative, impassive courage was evident in his rugged son, Denny.

Denny began racing an MG TC in New Zealand in 1957, then progressed via an MGA to 2-liter Cooper-Climax single-seaters in 1959. He and fellow Kiwi George Lawton jointly won the NZGPA's "Driver to Europe" scholarship for 1960, but poor Lawton crashed fatally on the tour at Roskilde, Denmark. Denny had a minor F1 drive at Snetterton, but then set about establishing himself in European Formula Junior racing through 1961-62.

He did well in the earliest Brabham FJ cars into 1963 and Jack gave him an F1 ride at Karlskoga, Sweden, that August. He finished fourth, began to shine in 1964 F2 and reappeared in Formula 1 at the 1965 British GP. When Dan Gurney quit the team to found his own Eagle operation for 1966, Denny Hulme became Jack Brabham's full-time No. 2.

After supporting his team leader brilliantly in both the works F1 and F2 cars through 1966, Denny began winning in '67 at Monaco, and then again at Nürburgring. Into the final Mexican GP the World Championship lay between the two Brabham team drivers, and Denny snatched the title from his boss.

Meanwhile, he had been driving CanAm sports-racing cars for fellow New Zealander Bruce McLaren, and for 1968 Denny became part of an all-Kiwi Formula 1 team, running new McLaren M7A cars with Cosworth-Ford V8 engines. Denny won the Canadian and Italian GPs and later the 1969 Mexican, but Bruce was killed testing a CanAm car in June 1970 and his bosom buddy was devastated.

"Denny the Bear" had been burned in an incident at Indianapolis – where he had competed in every 500 since 1967 – but he battled back without complaint to help the McLaren team survive and prosper into 1974. He won the 1972 South African GP, the 1973 Swedish and the 1974 Argentine before retiring from driving at the end of that season.

He returned to New Zealand but continued to race touring cars, and eventually trucks, with tremendous success, well into his 50s. He had been the most self-effacing of World Champions, one of the most private of all F1 legends, but tragedy dogged his family – his son Martin drowned and while driving in the Bathurst 1000 kms saloon car classic in Australia. In 1992 Denny suffered a massive heart attack, and all resuscitation attempts failed. He had seemed the most indestructible of great racing drivers. He was only 55.

LEFT: Denny Hulme drove for his fellow Kiwi Bruce McLaren's Formula 1 team from 1968 to the end of his frontline career in 1974. Here he shows how in the cutback "Monaco-nosed" McLaren M7A, entering the *Tabac* in the 1968 Monaco Grand Prix.

ABOVE RIGHT: "Denny the Bear" – the rugged Kiwi shone in Jack Brabham's Repco-engined works cars during 1966-67 and beat his team chief to the World Championship title that second season with performances which included victory in the German Grand Prix (RIGHT) in this Repco Brabham BT24, pictured here on the bumpy concrete banking of the Nürburgring's *Karussel*.

JOCHEN RINDT

1942-1970

The Austrian Jochen Rindt, raised by his maternal grandparents, was heir to a German spice dynasty fortune. He developed into a loudly independent, rebellious youth with a taste for preposterously colorful clothes and equally preposterously rapid road driving in a succession of costly cars.

After early success in saloon and minor-Formula cars, he attracted backing from Ford Austria for a 1964 F2 Brabham and that year he burst to prominence with tremendous drives in the important British F2 rounds at Mallory Park and Crystal Palace. He showed a clean pair of heels to all the established stars, including Jimmy Clark and Graham Hill, and Formula 1 beckoned.

Rob Walker gave him a guest drive in a Brabham-BRM in the Austrian GP at Zeltweg aerodrome, and Jochen then joined Cooper for 1965-67. Since Cooper had by that time fallen behind the pace in Formula 1, he would have a difficult three seasons at Grand Prix level, but meanwhile he became the uncrowned King of Formula 2 in his Roy Winkelmann Team Brabhams and won the 1965 Le Mans 24-Hours.

Jochen's driving style was explosively spectacular: brake late, power early, toss the steering, control the slide. Lap after lap a lurid accident would appear inevitable; lap after lap he would somehow get away with it. Then the trackside observers would realize this was simply the way Jochen drove – it was fun to watch, it was fast and he evidently found it terrific fun to do.

In 1968 Jochen left Cooper for Brabham but "Black Jack's" team used the new 4-cam Repco V8 engine that year which proved appallingly unreliable. Lotus had meanwhile lost the great Jim Clark, and so Colin Chapman outbid Brabham for Jochen's services, even though he was supicious of Colin's cavalier reputation and of Lotus frailty – their cars seemed to break too often.

Rindt and Chapman antagonized one another, and after the collapse of high-strutted wings upon both Lotuses in Barcelona – triggering two huge high-speed accidents – Rindt's suspicion of Chapman/Lotus engineering became even more intense and vocal.

At last class told, and Rindt scored his maiden GP victory in the United States event at Watkins Glen, and for 1970 Lotus introduced its advanced chisel-shaped Type 72 car. The new design took a little time to become race-worthy, but meantime Jochen won the Monaco GP – beating Jack Brabham on the final corner – and then won on merit in the 72 in Holland and Germany, and with luck in Britain and France.

The World Championship was his for the taking in the Italian GP at Monza, but during practice a front brake-shaft apparently snapped when Rindt was trying to decelerate from around 200mph into the difficult *Parabolica* corner. A poorly installed barrier and a floodlighting pillar demolished the Lotus's front end. The most exciting racing driver of the age did not survive.

JACKIE STEWART

1939-

If ever a racing driver changed the face of motor racing then it was Jackie Stewart. This dynamic, multi-talented Scot was a tough Clydesider from Dumbarton, and the son of the proprietor of a modest garage business. His elder brother, Jimmy, had been an effective racing driver for the Edinburgh-based *Ecurie Ecosse* sportscar team of the 1950s.

Born in 1939, in his youth Jackie had been more interested in clay pigeon shooting. As in everything he would attempt – with the exception of reading and writing (he was dyslexic) – Jackie was a natural competitor, and a natural winner.

He only narrowly missed selection for the Olympic shooting competition, and then began race driving. His first races were in a modest Marcos and then an E-type Jaguar owned by a customer of the Dumbuck garage, before he moved on to *Ecurie Ecosse*'s evil-handling Cooper Monaco. He drove that car so indecently fast that his name was suggested by Robin McKay – manager of the Goodwood race circuit in England – to Cooper minor-Formula team patron Ken Tyrrell as a prospect for 1964.

A new 1-liter F3 class was being launched that season, and in a winter test session at Goodwood the young Stewart set such shattering lap times, that he even bettered works Formula 1 driver Bruce McLaren's best in Tyrrell's latest F3 prototype.

Ken immediately signed-up the young Scot and during 1964 he and his Tyrrell utterly dominated

LEFT: The aggressive and fearless Austrian star Jochen Rindt found his feet in 3-liter Formula 1 handling the hefty and tiring Cooper-Maserati T81 V12s as here in the 1966 Dutch Grand prix at Zandvoort.

ABOVE RIGHT: Confident, ambitious, enormously gifted – young Jackie Stewart bulleted through Formula 3, Formula 2 and into Formula 1 all within one season – 1964.

RIGHT: With BRM for the first full F1 season in 1965 wee Jackie shone everywhere he appeared – here he is on the seafront at Monte Carlo in the superb BRM P261.

ABOVE: Mission accomplished – Jackie Stewart secured his maiden Driver's World Championship title with a typically intelligent, combative and ferociously fast performance in the 1969 Italian Grand Prix at Monza, driving Ken Tyrrell's Equipe Matra International Matra-Cosworth MS80.

LEFT: Older, fully established, Stewart the stylish businessman became the marketing men's dream World Champion Driver.

RIGHT: The second World title beckons – Jackie at his best in the superb Derek Gardner-designed Tyrrell in the 1971 French Grand Prix at Ricard-Castellet.

Formula 3. By high summer he was showing many old hands the way in Formula 2, and by season's end he was making his non-Championship Formula 1 debut in a works Lotus normally reserved for reigning World Champion Jimmy Clark.

For 1965 Jackie Stewart was then snapped up by the BRM team to become No. 2 to another World Champion – Graham Hill. With unstinting support from both these senior superstars, Stewart's meteoric career continued to incandesce.

Stewart scored World Championship points in his very first Grand Prix – in South Africa in 1965. He won his first F1 race – at that year's May Silverstone meeting, and his first World Championship GP – the Italian at Monza – by beating team leader Graham Hill across the line by inches.

In 1966 he won the Tasman Championship in New Zealand and Australia, driving a special BRM, and he made his debut in American Indycar racing, at Indianapolis where he looked set to win at one stage until his *Red Ball* Lola broke.

In Europe he won the Monaco GP for BRM but then crashed on the opening lap of the Belgian GP at Spa and was trapped in his car, in a cockpit flooding with fuel, before team-mate Hill – who had also crashed nearby – helped extricate him with a damaged collar bone. This frightening experience made "JYS," as he became known, hyper safety conscious.

He was already a vociferous advocate of driver-restraining seat belts, onboard fire extinguishing systems, and track-flanking Armco barriers – often to the intense disgust of traditionalist enthusiasts. Yet once he was happy that safety standards had been applied he would then – as one of his later American employers put it – "Really Stand On IT! Man, did he make a car Go!"

That he did. . . . After two poor BRM seasons handicapped by inadequate machinery through 1966-67, he joined Ken Tyrrell's new F1 team to run French-built Matra chassis with British Cosworth-Ford V8 power for 1968-69. He challenged strongly for the World Championship in 1968 – only losing the title to Graham Hill in the very last round (in Mexico) after winning the Dutch, German and U.S. GPs.

Critics of his safety campaigning should have been silenced by his heroic German GP-winning drive, in rain and mist on the majestic 14.2-mile Nürburgring, with a broken bone in one wrist supported by a plastic cast: this really was the stuff of legend. In 1969 he became World Champion with Matra wins in the South African, Spanish, Dutch, French, British and Italian Grands Prix.

As his Matras no longer conformed with Formula 1 regulations into 1970, Ken Tyrrell bought his superstar driver new March cars, while having his own new prototype Tyrrell-Cosworth tailored to Jackie late that year.

Despite the stop-gap March's limitations JYS won in Spain and toward the end of the season proved the new Tyrrell's promise.

In 1971 he enjoyed another season such as 1969. Utterly dominant, his Tyrrell was the car of the season just as he asserted his pre-eminence as *the* driver to beat. Victories in the Spanish, Monaco, French, British, German and Canadian GPs secured his second World Championship crown.

Despite injury, and sickness, in 1972 Jackie still won four more Grand Prix races finishing runner-up to new Champion Emerson Fittipaldi, and in 1973 he was back to his best. He won five Grands Prix in this season, first matching Jim Clark's career record of 25 World Cham-

pionship round wins and ultimately raising it to 27 with his final victory at Nürburgring. All this time Stewart had been planning to retire from driving as the reigning World Champion after what would have been his 100th Grand Prix – the United States event at Watkins Glen that October.

Sadly this was not to be. His young French teammate Francois Cevert was killed there in a gruesome practice accident, and after one final brief run the Tyrrell team withdrew from the race and Jackie Stewart's record-breaking career had ended, the great Scot retiring to a life as an international consultant. This three-time World Champion Driver is indisputably an all-time motor racing Great.

EMERSON FITTIPALDI

1946-

Born in São Paulo, Brazil, on December 12, 1946, this friendly Brazilian displayed a staggeringly high level of natural skill from the first day he appeared on a European stage in the English Formula Ford club racing class. This was hardly surprising since Emerson and his elder brother, Wilson, had grown up with racing in their veins. Their father, Wilson Sr., was Brazil's leading racing journalist and broadcaster, and from their infancy he had encouraged his sons to compete in karts and Formula Vee racing cars.

Emerson emerged in English Formula Ford driving a Merlyn car in 1969. He was earmarked instantly as a natural winner, and rocketed into Formula 3 with similar success, winning a Lotus F2 drive for 1970. Colin Chapman then gave him his F1 debut that July in a works Lotus 49, barely 18 months after Fittipaldi's arrival from Brazil.

In the German GP at Hockenheim, Emerson finished fourth to score his first World Championship points, and after team No. 1 Jochen Rindt crashed fatally at Monza, it was Fittipaldi who led Team Lotus and won the U.S. GP at Watkins Glen – only his fourth World Championship race. During 1971 his progress as Team Lotus No. 1 was arrested by a mid-season road accident and the realistic need to gain simple experience against the best in the racing world.

By 1972 he was fully developed as a Formula 1 driver, and he thrust his black-and-gold John Player Special Lotus 72s to a stunning series of nine wins and his first World Championship title. For 1973 Chapman organized his JPS "superteam" with Ronnie Peterson joining Fittipaldi but this simply split the winning between them and allowed Jackie Stewart to take his third Championship crown while Team Lotus dominated the Constructors' competition.

Marlboro sponsorship money then took Fittipaldi to McLaren, for whom in 1974 he accumulated Championship points, more with the shrewd calculation of an accountant than as a world-class racing driver, and after winning three more GPs, a string of good placings secured his second title.

LEFT: The third World Championship title – Jackie Stewart blistering his Tyrrell 006/2 around Monte Carlo during his wining drive in the 1973 Monaco Grand Prix – equalling Jimmy Clark's career record of 25 *Grande Epreuve* race victories.

RIGHT: New kid on the block – Brazilian star Emerson Fittipaldi rushed into Formula 1 in 1970 and became Team Lotus number one after Rindt's death at Monza. By 1972 in the John Player special-liveried Lotus 72s he was near-unbeatable and he took his first World Championship title.

LEFT: South American multiple World Champions both – the Argentine Juan Fangio with five titles to his name greets Emerson Fittipaldi after the Brazilian's victory for Lotus in the 1973 Argentine Grand Prix at Buenos Aires. "The Old Man" loved to see, and be involved with, the new boys following in the footsteps of his revered career.

RIGHT: Jacky Ickx – the gifted Belgian who became arguably a greater star in sportscar racing than in Formula 1 but who was second in the Championship chase in both 1969 and '70.

FAR RIGHT: Ickx loved the more demanding circuits and excelled upon them – such as Germany's Nurburgring and (here) the Austrian Osterreichring.

Through 1975 Lauda's Ferraris had a performance edge over Fittipaldi's McLarens, but he won the British GP and then astonished the racing world by quitting the team – to join brother Wilson's Brazilian-backed Copersucar F1 project.

It was a disaster. Emerson's still burgeoning talents went to waste in appallingly inadequate cars with few flashes of form until, at the end of 1980, he opted out of driving to run the family team. But as once lucrative sponsorship from the Brazilian state sugar cartel evaporated, what had become the Fittipaldi team struggled and then collapsed in 1982.

Emerson began driving IMSA endurance cars in the U.S., and then entered the Championship Auto Racing Team (CART) Indycar series. He found warmth, and fulfilment, and renewed financial security in America as his driving could effectively handle all Stateside opposition.

In 1989 he won the Indy 500 classic in a Pat Patrick Team Penske car and subsequently, driving for the factory Penske team, he provided Nigel Mansell's main opposition through the historic Championship season of 1993. At the age of 47, Emerson Fittipaldi is still going strong, a racer born and bred.

JACKY ICKX

1945-

Son of Belgian's leading motoring journalist, Pascal Ickx, this civilized patrician, and rather aloof man, burst onto the motor-racing scene as a gawky youth barely out of his teens in 1966. He had cut his competition teeth in motorcycle trials before showing tremendous prowess in a Lotus-Cortina saloon car. Aged just 22 he handled a Formula 2 Matra in the 1967 German GP at Nürburgring, displaying such flair he held a place in the top six among the leading F1 cars!

One of the first to recognize the young Belgian's tremendous class had been John Wyer – the hugely experienced former racing director of Aston Martin, the Ford GT40 program, and by that time masterminding his own Gulf-Mirage operation with GT40-based 5-liter Mirage GT cars. Under Wyer's wing, Ickx proved himself an immediate winner, a phenomenal wet-weather driver, and a sportscar pilot of the highest class.

Driving the Ken Tyrrell-managed Matras, he won the 1967 European F2 Championship, and drove a Cooper-Maserati in that year's Italian GP to finish sixth and score his maiden World Championship point. Enzo Ferrari gave him a drive in 1968; Jacky winning the French GP at Rouen, despite torrential rain, and he only lost his strong chance of winning the Drivers' title by crashing heavily during practice for the Canadian GP, breaking a leg.

Wyer's sportscar program sponsors, Gulf Oil, also backed the Brabham F1 team for 1969, and with their backing Ickx switched from suspect Ferrari V12 power to proven Cosworth-Ford V8 engines in Brabham chassis. He won the German and Canadian GPs and added victory at Le Mans in his Gulf-JW team GT40.

Ferrari lured him back for 1970 where he helped develop the magnificent new F1 flat-12 312B cars into race winners, and dominated the Austrian, Canadian and Mexican GPs, but he was unable to better the dead Jochen Rindt's points total from earlier that season.

Ickx's F1 fortunes wilted during 1971 but in '72 he won the German GP, again for Ferrari; his last victory at this level. As Ferrari flopped in 1973 he abruptly moved to an alternative berth alongside Ronnie Peterson at Team Lotus. He scored a brilliant wet-weather win in the 1974 Race of Champions at Brands Hatch but his rather remote character and independent ways had put the skids beneath his Formula 1 career.

An appalling half-season with Wolf-Williams in 1976 ended in his dismissal, and he then recouped some fading respect with Ensign only to crash badly in the U.S. GP at Watkins Glen.

He had meanwhile become a highly-prized fixture in the Porsche sportscar team and continued a phenomenal career as the uncrowned king of endurance racing, winning the Le Mans 24-Hours no fewer than five times. After retiring from serious full-time competition, he excelled in super-enduro events such as the trans-Saharan Paris-Dakar "Raid," but this second career was scarred by the ghastly experience of seeing his navigator fatally burned in a terrifying accident during the Egyptian Pharaoh Rally in 1990. Among Formula 1 legends who also shone in sportscar racing, Jacky Ickx was indisputably the best.

NIKI LAUDA

1949-

In his shrewdness, his cool grasp of necessity, his political skills, and transcendant driving prowess, Nikolaus Andreas Lauda resembled wily Jack Brabham. He was certainly one of the cleverest men in Formula 1 from the mid-'70s to the mid-'80s.

The son of wealthy Viennese parents, the little Austrian was an independent youth who learned his racing craft in saloon, Formula Vee and F3 cars before renting a works March F2 drive in 1971. It cost him a tidy amount, and for 1972 he borrowed a large sum of money from the *Raiffeisenkasse* Bank to rent a March F1 ride alongside Ronnie Peterson.

He looked like just another over-rich Continental kid, a rent-a-driver out of his depth in Formula 1. But away from the public eye, the March engineers found him remarkably adept at finding the best a car had to offer. He worked relentlessly hard, and his only aim was winning. Niki then talked himself into a BRM team test drive, out-performing established stars Regazzoni and Beltoise. With unfulfillable promises of bringing sponsorship money into the team, he won a BRM drive and set about proving himself quick enough to retain it upon driving merit.

He did just that, earned the admiration of Enzo Ferrari, and transferred to Maranello for 1974, having to reach a financial settlement with BRM. In that new season he shone for Ferrari – winning the Spanish and Dutch GPs, and losing others through inexperience after leading. By 1975 he was fully mature – one of the fastest, most perceptive, best focussed, and competent drivers of his day. He won five GPs and the World Championship title.

Through 1976 he fought a protracted duel with James Hunt and McLaren, until his Ferrari broke on the opening lap of the German GP at Nürburgring and he barely survived a high-speed crash, multiple collision, and raging fire which left him disfigured for life.

LEFT: Niki Lauda had a tremendous impact upon the Formula 1 scene when he transferred from BRM to Ferrari and played a crucial role in developing Mauro Forghieri's latest *Tipo* 312B3 design into a race winner.

RIGHT: "The Rat" – Lauda neither made nor allowed any compromises in his approach to motor racing and welded Ferrari around him in a manner virtually without precedent between 1974 and 1977. The result was two World Championship titles for himself and an unprecedented three consecutive Constructors' crowns for Ferrari between 1975 and 1977.

LEFT: Niki at his best, winning the 1975 Monaco Grand Prix in the latest Ferrari 312T with its 3-liter flat-12 engine and distinctive *periscopica* tall engine airbox scoop.

ABOVE: The Austrian superstar entered racing despite parental opposition, borrowed money to pay his own way into Formula 1 and was ultimately paid millions to stay in it – and indeed ultimately to return to it! Few cleverer minds have ever graced the Grand Prix scene.

BELOW: Lauda makes a remarkable comeback in the Italian Grand Prix after his horrific accident at the Nürburgring earlier in the year.

This amazing young man willed himself back into racing after missing only two GPs, staving off James Hunt's Championship charge until the final round in Japan. There it poured with torrential rain, Niki – his burned eyelids hampering his vision – pulled out after the opening lap, abdicating his title chances.

He was pilloried by the Italian sporting press and Enzo Ferrari clearly doubted his Austrian star's ability to shine again. But Lauda's response was typical – no drama, he simply did a better job on the track. He won the South African GP and the German and Dutch, regained his World Champion title, then abruptly left Ferrari to join Brabham-Alfa Romeo for 1978.

These new cars were powerful and fast, but fuel-heavy and unreliable. The legendary Brabham "Fan-Car" gave Niki victory on its one-off appearance in the 1978 Swedish GP, and he was awarded victory at Monza after two cars which finished ahead of him were penalized for jumping the start.

He had become an obsessively intense private flyer. His ambitions extended to running his own airline and he founded Lauda Air. Then he suddenly found motor racing unfulfilling and walked away from it in the middle of practice for the 1979 Canadian GP.

He stayed away for two seasons before being persuaded to return in 1982, joining Ron Dennis' new McLaren International team. "The Rat" as he was nicknamed – or "that devious little mouse" – then won his third comeback GP at Long Beach, and for 1984 was teamed with Alain Prost and secured his third World title by half a point, in that year's final race.

In 1985 he scored his last Grand Prix victory – the Dutch at Zandvoort – thereafter doing his best to assist team-mate Prost to his first World title and then bowing out for good, concentrating upon Lauda Air and rejoining Ferrari as a part-time team management consultant in the early 1990s.

Niki's press conference address after his victory in the 1984 French GP says it all. He simply barked "Car *gut*, engine *gut*, Lauda *gut*! Any kvestions?" A no-nonsense superstar, who never suffered fools gladly.

RONNIE PETERSON

1944-1978

Motor racing, like any hyper-competitive first-class sport, does not in modern times foster warm amicability and mutual respect among its leading exponents. Ronnie Peterson was a gentle giant, soft, lazily relaxed, a bear of a man who at his best became the standard-setting driver of his time – yet still appeared not to have an enemy in the world.

Ronnie was the laid-back son of a baker, a mild-mannered tropical fish enthusiast who grew horns and a tail once strapped into a racing car, engine running,

pedal to the metal. Ronnie would describe his race driving style as *"Fladdout – I yust love to drive fladdout."* That indeed is what he did, and from the trackside his commitment and enjoyment were equally apparent – his car would visibly be straining every sinew to resist the braking, acceleration and cornering loads which he habitually applied. His was a win-or-bust style which endeared him to mechanic, spectator and rival driver alike. Ronnie was absolutely "A Racer," and everybody respected him for it.

He had aspired to European Championship level in racing karts before graduating into Formula 3 with an Italian Tecno chassis. In 1969 he drove the prototype F3 March in its maiden race, and in 1970 was given a private F1 March drive for Colin Crabbe's tiny Antique Automobiles team. He scored Championship points and led the works March F1 and F2 teams for the 1971-72 seasons.

Grand Prix victory eluded him, but no fewer than five second places and fastest laps told the story, while he dominated Formula 2 in the style of its former – and late – uncrowned king Jochen Rindt.

Colin Chapman then took Ronnie into his John Player Special "superteam" for 1973, as joint number one with reigning Champion Emerson Fittipaldi. It took Lotus time to reinforce its Type 72 cars sufficiently to survive the loads generated by Ronnie's rumbustious

LEFT: Ronnie Peterson was a driver who would give his all in any kind of racing car – good ones, bad ones, and downright misguided ones. Here he is trying his hardest in one of the latter – the tricky March 721X of 1972, in that year's Belgian Grand Prix run at the despised, misbegotten and never used again Nivelles autodrome.

RIGHT: Ronnie in one of the March cars in which he made his name, 1970-1972. By this time driver safety requirements had dictated the adoption of multi-layer fire-resistant protective overalls and balaclavas, driver restraint harnesses, and onboard fire-extinguishing systems as standard, plus far-reaching regulations governing car construction.

driving. Until they did he had a succession of pole positions and often led races until early race retirement. Once they did the trick, Ronnie notched his first Grand Prix victory in the French event at Ricard-Castellet, and won again in Austria, Italy and the U.S.

Through 1974 the Lotus 72 was really obsolescent, yet Ronnie rocketed the car to three classic race wins at Monaco, Dijon-Prenois and Monza. Lotus lost their grip through 1975 and early in '76 Ronnie returned to March – to win another Italian GP. The Elf fuel and oil company bought his services for the six-wheeled Tyrrell cars of 1977, to which he never adapted and which had in any case lost the edge demonstrated in '76.

Backed by his friend the wealthy Italian Count "Googie" Zanon, "SuperSwede" then rejoined Team Lotus for 1978 – accepting secondary status to Mario Andretti in their trend-setting Type 78 and 79 cars of ground-effect aerodynamic design. These machines dominated Formula 1, with Ronnie tracking Andretti everywhere, and the two achieved a series of Team 1-2 results with the Swede victorious in the South African and Austria Grands Prix.

But immediately after the start of the Italian GP at Monza, Ronnie's Lotus 78 was nudged into a high-speed curving slide by James Hunt's dodging McLaren, and it hurtled head-on into a trackside barrier against which its front end and cockpit sides collapsed, shattering the much-loved Swede's long legs.

Bone marrow was released into his bloodstream, and clots claimed his life next morning in Milan's Niguarda Hospital. His lovely wife, Barbro, was widowed and their daughter Nina left fatherless. Barbro never forgot Ronnie – and just before Christmas 1987, she was found dead in tragic circumstances at her home in England.

LEFT: It took several races early in 1973 and a great deal of testing experience before Team Lotus fully appreciated the tremendous loadings to which Ronnie Peterson subjected their latest Type 72 cars. As team chief Colin Chapman put it: "We finally prepared a car strong enough for him – and Ronnie began winning races. . . ." The 1973 French Grand Prix, here at Ricard-Castellet, was "SuperSwede's" first.

RIGHT: Ronnie – quiet, thoughtful, slow to move and quick to smile – the tropical fish enthusiast who doted upon his lovely wife Barbro and their daughter.

JAMES HUNT

1947-1993

Tall, fair-haired, the most free of free spirits, James Hunt was in many ways the natural successor to the old yah-hoo image which Mike Hawthorn had elevated to World Champion status in the 1950s. Hunt was an ex-public school boy – from Wellington College – son of a London stockbroker, who subordinated any ideas he may ever have had about respectability and a comfortably secure business career to his burning ambition to become a successful racing driver.

He found his feet in the hurly-burly of Formula Ford in the late 1960s before graduating to Formula 3 where he first earned his nickname of "Hunt the Shunt" after innumerable examples of over-commitment – bravery exceeding brain, they said.

By the start of 1972, James Hunt was in danger of

being left on the margins, a hopeless case, but he was rescued by the enthusiastic young Lord Alexander Hesketh who provided him with a Formula 2 March drive and then, in 1973, with an F1 debut in a hired Surtees at the Brands Hatch Race of Champions.

James finished third, astonishing many critics. They had to admit he really had driven rather well. Hesketh then acquired a March 731 "kit" plus the services of former factory engineer Dr. Harvey Postlethwaite. The car developed rapidly and Hunt's driving matured into intelligently-applied, relentless *speed*.

He finished fourth in the British GP and set fastest race lap, third at Zandvoort and ultimately a brilliant second in the U.S. GP at Watkins Glen – all in a car which nobody else rated. James joked that he had merely asked Harvey "to make it quick along the straight and I'll block 'em all off through the corners"! But there was much more to it than that, and Hunt, Harvey and Hesketh grew together as a splendidly tight-knit, gung-ho and very British team.

For 1974 Postlethwaite created the Hesketh 308 car for James to drive, but unreliability and driver errors prevented the team from achieving serious success until 1975, when the habitually tee-shirted, sandal-wearing Englishman won the Dutch GP after a clever tactical race. However, Hesketh's purse was almost empty, and when Emerson Fittipaldi quit McLaren for Copersucar, Hunt took his place as McLaren No. 1 for 1976.

He shone. He was brilliant, yet always tense and hyper; so nervous before a race that he could vomit – and sometimes he would be ill again within the car – a bundle of nervous energy funneled into speed. He qualified on pole position for the new 1976 season's opening Brazilian GP, he won in Spain but was disqualified on a technicality and then reinstated later in the year, upon appeal. That season became a classical confrontation between Hunt for McLaren and Niki Lauda for Ferrari, and after crashing on lap one of the British GP at Brands Hatch, James took the restart in his repaired car and won, only to be disqualified again on a technicality – a sentence in this case made to stick.

He then won the German GP in which Lauda was injured, and was handicapped in the Italian race by dubious fuel sample juggling on the part of the governing authorities. By this time his duel with Lauda and Ferrari had become a ferocious crusade – though personally he and Niki remained upon good terms – James dominated the Canadian and U.S. GPs and then stole the World title with third place after delays in a sensational, rain-flooded Japanese GP at Fuji.

In 1977 James won the British GP, then faded badly through 1978 – "going through the motions" his team chief believed. The old obsessive fire and urge had evaporated. For 1979 Hunt joined Walter Wolf's team but detested contemporary ground-effects cars and after the Monaco GP he announced his retirement.

He had many business interests and for more than a decade provided a popular commentating foil to the BBC's Murray Walker on TV Grand Prix coverage. But in many ways his private life and business lives became a shambles, and in the summer of 1993 what we all believed to have been James' enormous heart, failed him – and the last British World Champion for 16 long years was found dead at his home in Wimbledon.

TOP LEFT: James Hunt – in 1976 he became Britain's last World Champion before Nigel Mansell's great success of 1992. Like Mike Hawthorn before him, James was an extrovert fun-lover of independent persuasion who had his darker side . . .

LEFT: The first of 92 Grands Prix for Hunt at Monaco in 1973 in Lord Hesketh's privately-entered March 731. James's embryo Formula 1 career prospered as the car was progressively developed for him by team engineer Harvey Postlethwaite.

RIGHT: 1976 World Champion Driver – James Hunt and the Marlboro-sponsored works McLaren-Cosworth M23.

MARIO ANDRETTI

1940-

American motor racing has a very different cultural background to its European counterpart. The traditional accent in America has been upon short-length oval tracks; the European emphasis upon closed road-type circuits. Mario Andretti, born in Trieste, Italy, in the early days of World War II and taken to the U.S. as a teenage immigrant, had roots in both camps. He had seen some of the great Italian road races of the 1950s but began race driving in the U.S. and developed his immense skills there into the 1960s. He would say with typical honesty that while his heart was in European-style road racing, his wallet depended upon U.S. track racing.

Mario first made his mark in Europe with the Ford GT Le Mans team, and had also appeared in road-racing Ferraris when Lotus offered him an F1 debut in the 1968 U.S. GP at Watkins Glen. Mario promptly qualified his unfamiliar works Lotus 49 on pole position! In 1969 he took in as many GPs for Lotus as his his Indycar commitments would allow, and in 1970 he tackled a full F1

program in an uncompetitive STP-liveried March car. He was also handling sportscars for Ferrari, and in 1971-72 drove works F1 Ferraris whenever available and won the South African GP.

His Stateside commitments prevented a full F1 season until the U.S. GP in October 1974, when he gave the new Vel's Parnelli Team USA F1 car its promising debut. The VPJ team then struggled in F1 through 1975 and finally folded in '76, when Mario rejoined Team Lotus for a serious F1 program.

He won the Japanese GP, and in 1977 in Colin Chapman's revolutionary Lotus 78 "wing car," he won four more GPs and came within an ace of World Championship victory. For 1978 Team Lotus built a better "ground-effects" car – the Type 79 – and Mario was dominant due to Ronnie Peterson's "runner-up" understanding with Chapman. So "SuperWop" as the tough, yet gentlemanly, old Italian was known, became World Champion.

But Lotus flopped through 1979-80 and Andretti floundered with them. For 1981 he moved to Alfa Romeo – no longer the dominant Italian team of his boyhood – and he abandoned Formula 1 at the end of that season, to concentrate upon Indycar competition, although guesting for Williams at Long Beach, California in 1982.

After Villeneuve's death and Didier Pironi's career-ending accident at Hockenheim, Mario answered an emotional invitation from Enzo Ferrari to lead the revamped team at Monza. He qualified on pole, put perhaps 30,000 on the Italian GP raceday gate, and finished third. At the subsequent Las Vegas race his F1 career then ended in ignominious suspension failure.

Mario continued racing in Indycars – and still does so into 1994, approaching his mid-50s – the U.S.'s "Mr. Motor Racing," and proud father of former National Champion, Michael Andretti.

LEFT: 1978 World Champion Mario Andretti in the epochal Lotus 79 with its ground-effects aerodynamic under-surfaces, leading that year's British Grand Prix at Brands Hatch. Italian-born Mario was a popular figure who brought enormous experience and racecraft into Formula 1 after twenty years of competition. He was the first American to win the title since Phil Hill in 1961.

RIGHT: 1979 World Champion Jody Scheckter was the first South African to take the crown – his prior experience included Grand Prix-winning drives in the stagering 1976 six-wheeled Tyrrell P34.

JODY SCHECKTER

1950-

A profoundly competitive, fit, strong and athletic South African, Jody Scheckter made his name as a daring and aggressive young Formula Ford driver in his home country before exploding onto the British club racing scene in 1971.

His progress via Formula Ford 1600 Merlyn and F3 into a works McLaren M23 F1 car in the 1972 United States GP was as meteoric as had been Jackie Stewart's in 1963-64. In 1973, making another early McLaren appearance in the French GP at Ricard, Jody actually led at phenomenal speed before being thumped from behind by a frustrated Emerson Fittipaldi's Lotus 72.

The following race was the British GP at Silverstone. Jody qualified well in his Yardley-McLaren but pressed too hard completing the opening lap, ran wide onto the grass before the main grandstand, and then spun backward into the pit wall, triggering an almighty multiple collision, causing the race to be red-flagged almost before it had begun.

James Hunt christened him "Fletcher" after the young fledgling of the Jonathan Livingstone Seagull story who tried to fly high before he was capable, and who crashed repeatedly into the cliffside. It was apt, and it stuck – "Fletcher" he became.

But his pace and talent were unmistakable. For 1974 Ken Tyrrell teamed him with Patrick Depailler following the retirement of Jackie Stewart and death of François Cevert.

Chief Engineer Derek Gardner designed an all-new Tyrrell with forgiving handling, easier for relatively inexperienced young men to race hard in security. Jody matured into a race winner – he took the Swedish and British GPs, had a chance of the World title into the final round at Watkins Glen, NY, and finished a very close third in the table.

In 1975 he scored a home win at Kyalami, outside Johannesburg, and in '76 handled the weird-looking but rapid 6-wheeled Tyrrells to such effect that he won the Swedish Grand Prix at Anderstorp.

Canadian oilman-cum-racing enthusiast Walter Wolf then recruited Jody for his new F1 team in 1977, and he won in the brand-new Harvey Postlethwaite-designed car upon its debut – straight out of the box – in Argentina. Further Wolf success followed at Monaco and in Canada, and Jody almost won the World title, pipped into second place, this time by Niki Lauda.

Wolf Racing then flopped through 1978 and Ferrari teamed Scheckter with the relatively inexperienced Gilles Villeneuve for 1979. Jody won the Belgian, Monaco and Italian GPs and at last secured the Drivers' World Championship title which had so narrowly eluded him for so long.

In 1980 Ferrari ran their long-faithful 3-liter flat-12 engine for just one final season while investing heavily in the long-term development of a 1500cc turbocharged V6 unit for 1981. Their T5 flat-12 car was a fairly appalling machine and the instinctive skills of neither Scheckter nor Villeneuve could do much with it. Jody's motivation evaporated, he failed even to quality for the Canadian GP, and retired at season's end, ultimately settling in Atlanta, Georgia, as a bustling – and still highly competitive – businessman.

ALAN JONES

1946-

Physical fitness, great strength, steely determination and the formidable ability to apply relentless pressure until an opponent's nerve would crack, made Alan Jones into Australia's second World Champion Driver after Jack Brabham.

"Jonesie's" father, Stan, had been a leading Australian racing driver throughout the 1950s and Alan found his way into British club racing in the early 1970s before making his F1 debut in a private Hesketh in 1975. He seemed no more than a merely competent journeyman driver from Down-under, enjoying his day in the sun. But he drove for Surtees through 1976 and then joined Shadow for '77 and, when the fates smiled, he won the Austrian GP!

Suddenly, Alan Jones looked like more than just another journeyman. He was good at race-engineering his cars to exploit their best potential, and his strength of character and determination to succeed impressed Frank Williams who gave him a drive for 1978. His car was the latest arrow-head shaped Williams FW06 created by Patrick Head. It was conventional, but commonsensical; beautifully made – and fast. It became the best of the 1978 conventional cars chasing the dominant new Lotus 79s with their ground-effect aerodynamic systems, and second place in the U.S. GP proved the promise of the Jones/Williams partnership.

For 1979 Head produced a better ground-effects car than Lotus's – the Williams FW07 – which became the dominant force that season. Alan drove typically hard, and once reliability had been achieved, he won the German, Austrian, Dutch and Canadian GPs and just missed the World Championship title.

He put this right in 1980, during a terrific season-long duel with Nelson Piquet – winning six times and clinching the title in Canada. But for a string of disappointing car problems, he might have retained his title in 1981, but after winning the Las Vegas GP at season's end he retired, saying that modern "solid suspension" F1 cars no longer appealed to him.

He raced Porsches in Australia through 1982 then made a brief F1 comeback in 1983, handling an Arrows at Long Beach, California. After a further sabbatical, he was then signed-up for the new Ford-backed Haas-Lola FORCE F1 team of 1985, but the project floundered and "Jonesie" could not overcome the problems alone. He looked a spent force. Which was a pity – because at his best he had been superb.

LEFT: Jones winning the 1980 British GP at Brands Hatch in his Williams FW07B.

ABOVE: "Jonesie" had begun his Grand Prix career in 1975 as a baby-faced 28-year-old, first in a Hesketh, then in an Embassy-Hill team Lola.

RIGHT: Kerb-rider – Gilles Villeneuve in a 1979 Ferrari 312T4.

GILLES VILLENEUVE

1950-1982

Few racing drivers have ever displayed more visible fire and passion than this diminutive – tragically ill-fated – French-Canadian.

Like Ronnie Peterson before him, Gilles believed the only way to drive fast was with complete commitment, flat-out all the way – almost hang the consequences. This was either sheer genius, a wonderful display of sporting commitment, or the brainless act of a mindless racing animal. Since to finish first one must first finish, brilliant driving alone cannot compensate for an inability to stay the distance. Gilles Villeneuve would win only six Grand Prix races which was a rather ordinary record by modern top-line standards, and he was undoubtedly often the architect of his own downfall.

His taste for motorized competition had been honed upon snowmobiles in Canada before he hit the motor sporting headlines with victory at the Trois Rivières Formula Atlantic race of 1976. James Hunt finished third as a guest-driver there and returned to England raving about the young French-Canadian's pace.

The following summer saw McLaren providing Gilles with his F1 debut, in a third M23 car for the British GP at Silverstone. He finished tenth but impressed many. As Niki Lauda walked out of Ferrari with two late-season GPs remaining on the calendar, Villeneuve was invited to replace him. He flew, literally, in Japan after a terrifying collision with Ronnie Peterson's six-wheeled Tyrrell.

In 1978 he led the Long Beach GP, then notched his maiden win on his home Canadian GP circuit at Montreal. For 1979 he was teamed with Jody Scheckter and won the South African, Long Beach and U.S. GPs. Always an honorable man, his deal with Ferrari was to play a supporting role to Scheckter, and he did that dutifully, staying behind the South African at Monza in

a Ferrari 1-2 which – had the order been reversed – could have brought him the World title instead.

The next year was a season best forgotten by Ferrari fans but Villeneuve kept hammering away spectacularly upon the very edge of control. He was looking forward to 1981 when the team's new 1500cc turbocharged V6 projectiles would be ready. "No point in sitting back," he said, "because when the new cars are ready we will have forgotten how to drive fast."

In 1981 the new Ferrari 126C turbo cars remained evil-handling but were phenomenally fast along the straight – so Villeneuve perfected the art of baulking his rivals around the corners to win at Monaco and Jarama, Spain.

Gilles had dominated his team-mate Didier Pironi through 1981, but the determined Frenchman pressed ever harder in new Ferrari 126C2 cars early in 1982. When Pironi passed Villeneuve against team orders to win the San Marino GP at Imola, Gilles felt betrayed and was outraged. He never spoke to Pironi again, and two weeks later, trying to better the Frenchman's qualifying time for the Belgian GP at Zolder, he collided with a slower car and was sent somersaulting to a tragically premature death.

JACQUES LAFFITE

1943-

If gallic flair and charm is a virtue then Jacques Laffite – the former race mechanic-turned-Formula 1 driver – was a most virtuous man.

"Jolly Jacques" was warm-hearted and humorous, highly popular, and a hard-charging racer on his day. He found his way into motor racing through his friend, driver Jean-Pierre Jabouille, for whom he acted as F3 mechanic, and they subsequently married two sisters, becoming brothers-in-law.

Jacques fought hard to make his own mark as a driver in Formula 3, his class career highlighted by victory in a Martini car in the F3 race supporting the 1973 Monaco GP. Frank Williams then provided his Formula 1 debut in 1974, and while Frank ran his tiny team from a telephone box and struggled to meet his engine rebuild bill, Laffite just drove their uncompetitive cars

ever better. A lucky second place in the 1975 German GP secured the team's short-term future and elated Jacques and Frank alike.

Jacques had also been building his reputation in sportscar racing, notably with Matra-Simca, Alpine-Renault; and Alfa Romeo, and for 1976 Guy Ligier invited him to lead his new all-French F1 team, using Matra V12 engines. Laffite notched his maiden victory in the 1977 Swedish GP and for 1979, with Cosworth-Ford V8 power and new ground-effect design chassis, the Ligier team briefly set the technical pace in Formula 1, Jacques winning the season-opening Argentine and Brazilian GPs.

The Frenchmen then lost their way. Jacques could not win again until the 1980 German GP and for 1981-82 Ligier reverted to Matra power under the "Talbot" name – Jacques winning the Austrian and Canadian GPs and running the World title close.

Jacques then rejoined Williams for 1983-84 and the Anglophile Laffite actually rented the Stoke Poges mansion formerly home to Tony Vandervell – creator of the 1950s Vanwall F1 team. He was by this time ageing and past his best, but he was still a hugely popular sportsman. Honda's turbocharged V6 engines adopted by Williams for '84 exposed his failing talents – and hunger – and Jacques returned to Ligier for 1985-86.

The British GP at Brands Hatch would see him equal Graham Hill's career record of 176 GPs, but in a start-line *melee* the unfortunate Frenchman rammed a barrier head-on, the impact shattering both his legs. This spelled a sorry end to his Formula 1 career, but he would return to race driving, in his 40s, in saloon cars, and the broad smile seldom waned.

ABOVE LEFT: Gilles Villeneuve became a cult figure and a virtual folk hero for motor racing fans of the late-'70s and early-'80s with a string of spectacular Formula 1 drives for Ferrari. Enzo Ferrari himself described him as "the new Nuvolari."

LEFT: Gilles revelled in the ferocious horsepower of the new turbocharged Ferrari 126C in 1981 and fought some remarkable battles with the design's notoriously deficient handling to win both the Monaco and Spanish GPs.

RIGHT: French star "Jolly Jacques" Laffite rounding Druid's Hairpin in his ear-splitting V12-engined Ligier-Talbot at the 1982 British Grand Prix at Brands Hatch.

NELSON PIQUET

1952-

Born Nelson Soutomaior in 1952 in Rio de Janeiro, Brazil, this three-time World Champion adopted his mother's maiden name – Piquet – as being easier on race commentators' tonsils. His wealthy father had great ambitions for his son in top-class tennis, Nelson spending part of his youth in California undergoing intensive tennis coaching.

But it was wheeled sports which really fired him, and after shining in Brazilian national karting, motorcycle racing and Formula Vee, he headed for Europe in 1977 and was placed third in the European F3 Championship, driving a British Ralt car.

In 1978 he aimed at the prestigious British F3 title,

won 13 races and resoundingly clinched the Championship. Morris Nunn of Ensign gave him his F1 debut in that year's German GP, after which he drove a private McLaren M23 in the last three European F1 rounds.

Bernie Ecclestone of Brabham recognized Piquet's glittering potential and gave him a drive in the last GP of that year, then a regular place as Lauda's No 2 for 1979. When Niki bowed-out of racing without warning in Canada late that season, Nelson emerged as *de facto* Brabham team leader, having been quicker than Niki.

Early in 1980 he won the Long Beach GP in the latest Brabham-Cosworth Ford BT49 and added victories in Holland and Italy, just missing out on the World title which went to his great rival, Alan Jones of Williams.

Nelson forged a great working relationship with Brabham designer Gordon Murray, and in 1981 they engineered World Championship victory, Nelson clinching the title in the final round at Las Vegas. For 1982 Brabham turned to BMW turbocharged motive power and a string of spectacular engine failures left the defending Champion with only a single victory.

Nelson had a rare mechanical sympathy which contributed greatly to BMW engine development, and in 1983 his commitment, skill, and intelligent speed secured a second Drivers' Championship for himself and another title for Brabham, the first at the top level for BMW.

Nelson stayed with Brabham through 1984-85, but top-class success eluded the fading team and its Brazilian number one who was enjoying life hugely

LEFT: Nelson Piquet – the happy-go-lucky Brazilian – loved a challenge, and developing the turbocharged 4-cylinder BMW-powered Brabham BT50 into a race winner as reigning World Champion during 1982 certainly provided that. Here in the year's French Grand Prix at Ricard-Castellet he led for 16 rumbustious laps.

ABOVE RIGHT: Nelson Piquet in the 1983 Monaco Grand Prix during his second World Championship-winning year.

RIGHT: There was little love lost between Piquet and Nigel Mansell as team-mates in the Williams-Honda team of 1986. Here Nelson comes under intense pressure from the Briton at Brands Hatch.

away from the racing scene. Then, abruptly, Piquet moved to Williams-Honda for 1986, almost winning another Drivers' title and publicly blaming his failure upon Williams' reluctance to make team-mate Nigel Mansell play a purely supporting role.

Alain Prost of McLaren had denied Piquet the Championship in the final race at Adelaide, and still Nelson accumulated points toward a third Championship through 1987, very much in the calculating "places-are-good-enough" manner of his countryman – Emerson Fittipaldi – through '74.

When Honda abandoned Williams for Lotus at the end of 1987, Piquet moved with their engines. For 1988 with Camel sponsorship, Honda V6 turbo power and reigning Champion Piquet as No. 1, Team Lotus appeared to have it all. Events proved otherwise – the chassis was appalling and Piquet seemingly uninterested. Honda took their engines elsewhere, leaving Lotus with Judd V8s for 1989. Nelson felt he no longer had any chance of winning and merely attended races.

It was sad to see. But for 1990 he signed a payment-by-results contract with Benetton-Ford. Highly motivated, intensely focused, the old Piquet flair returned as he accumulated wins in three highly lucrative GPs.

Without a top-class offer for 1992 he then accepted an Indycar drive in the US, tackling the Indianapolis 500 speedway classic. But an ugly practice accident there shattered both his legs and crushed his feet; the finest medical help rebuilt them and after announcing he would never ever drive a racing car again – sure enough – he came back. But not, sadly, as the dazzling star he had once been.

ABOVE: Nelson Piquet – World Champion 1981, 1983 and 1987 – during his Brabham days, sponsored by the Italian Parmalet dairy company.

LEFT: Turbocharged technology from Honda of Japan propelled Williams to the Constructors' World titles of 1986-87 and Nelson to the Drivers' crown in 1987.

RIGHT: Keke Rosberg and Williams had fought a rearguard action for Cosworth-Ford's naturally-aspirated 3-liter engines through 1982, stealing the Drivers' title from the far more potent 1½-liter turbocharged brigade.

FAR RIGHT: Where instinctive car control was concerned, Keke Rosberg, the rugged Finn, had few peers.

KEKE ROSBERG

1948-

Built like a beach lifeguard, broad-shouldered Keijo "Keke" Rosberg spent years in becoming an overnight success. After long seasons excelling in minor Formulae cars around Europe, New Zealand, Australia and North America, the flying Swedish-born Finn made his F1 debut in Hong Kong millionaire Teddy Yip's private Theodore-Cosworth Ford car in 1978, winning the flooded International Trophy non-Championship race at Silverstone in great style after the usual front-runners had slithered off into the boondocks.

Rosberg's greatest asset had always been sheer, instinctive car control and the touch and balance displayed as he knife-edged the Theodore around streaming Silverstone – finding grip where essentially there should have been none – impressed all observers.

In 1979 he drove for the wobbling Wolf team and in 1980-81 for moribund Fittipaldi. Some day the break would come and sure enough for 1982 after Alan Jones's abrupt retirement Frank Williams needed a decent driver – Keke was available, and filled the bill.

Armed at last with a competitive car, Rosberg took his chance with both strong hands and bullied his Cos-worth-Ford 3-liter car around to a string of high points-scoring finishes behind the inherently faster, but less reliable, 1500cc turbocharged opposition. Would he become the first driver ever to win the World title without winning a single race outright? This seemed distinctly possible until he triumphed in the so-called "Swiss" GP at Dijon in France, clinching the title in the final round at Las Vegas, Nevada.

In 1983 he won the Monaco GP for Williams, and as they adopted Honda V6 turbo power for 1984 he helped develop the cars and notched the new partnership's first F1 victory in the unique Dallas GP in Texas.

Those Williams-Hondas were fire-breathing, tricky to drive, wheel-spinning projectiles with explosive power demanding the most split-second perception and throttle control. Rosberg had that – his hapless teammate Jacques Laffite did not. It showed.

In 1985, teamed with Nigel Mansell, Keke won twice more – at Detroit and Adelaide – before replacing Niki Lauda alongside Prost at McLaren-TAG Turbo for '86. With typical honesty, Keke made the famous observation: "I thought I was the fastest driver in the world until I joined Alain Prost at McLaren." He wanted the smooth-handling cars altered to suit his chuck-it-and-catch driving style but engineer John Barnard resisted his requests, knowing Prost's way was faster. Ultimately a compromise was reached, and Rosberg became happier. However, this came too late for his own World Championship hopes, and he happily became a team player to support Prost's double-title chance in the final GPs of that year.

He had decided to retire, and did so, but four years later he donned overalls and helmet again to lead Peugeot's World Sportscar Championship team in 1991, then handled a Mercedes saloon in the 1992 German Touring Car Championship – while pursuing his own multifarious business interests, and fostering the careers of young Scandinavian drivers with Formula 1 ambitions – perhaps to build legends of the future?

RICCARDO PATRESE

1954-

The most experienced Grand Prix driver of all time, by the end of the 1993 season, Riccardo Patrese had driven in more than 200 World Championship-qualifying races – 24 more than Graham Hill and Jacques Laffite in joint second place with 176 GPs each.

Yet during his first seasons in Formula 1, Riccardo had been regarded by many of his peers as a liability at such a level. He earned an ugly reputation as a weaver, a wheel-tangler, a blocker, a shover. A naturally shy, reserved young man, he was liable to respond to criticism in blunt, dismissive and sometimes crude Italian. That he developed from such a background to become a charming, relaxed and uncomplicated member of the F1 circus is enormously to his credit, and speaks volumes for the skill with which his later teams – most notably Brabham and Williams, handled this sensitive, and very Italian, personality.

Another recruit from F3 and F2, Patrese made his F1 debut in the Shadow team of 1977 and then showed great promise in the brand-new splinter-group Arrows project of '78. He was vilified as the supposed cause of that year's Italian GP start accident which caused Ronnie Peterson's tragic death, and a disgraceful campaign by his fellow drivers prevented his participation in the following U.S. GP at Watkins Glen. Only extensive photographic evidence cleared his name and all but one of those drivers who had so wrongly condemned him later apologized and made their peace.

Regardless, mud stuck, Patrese suffered it, and his aggressive driving continued to invite censure and criticism not only in Formula 1, but also in sportscar competition, most notably with the Lancia Corse factory team.

In 1982 Riccardo joined Bernie Ecclestone's Brabham team as No. 2 to Nelson Piquet. Ecclestone began molding the man who went on to F1 victory in the Monaco GP that year. In 1983 he won the South African GP to clinch the Championship titles for Piquet and Brabham-BMW, but thereafter Formula 1 was a fallow field for him for the next five years.

Patrese struggled with Alfa Romeo through 1984-85, then returned to Brabham-BMW in 1986-87. His career appeared to be approaching its natural conclusion, when Frank Williams teamed him with Nigel Mansell in the 1988 Williams-Judds.

With proper massaging of that fragile ego and friendly family support from all the Didcot team, Riccardo began to feel respected, and at home. When Renault's V10 engine emerged for 1989 the resurgent Patrese became a serious contender. He won the 1990 San Marino GP and in 1991 won the Mexican and Spanish GPs and took pole positions and fastest laps. Through 1992 he played an admirable supporting role to Mansell – despite perhaps pressing too hard for team comfort in some races – but whenever Mansell's car failed Patrese was normally there to salvage maximum Constructors' points for his team.

He was a round-peg in a round hole until Mansell split from Williams at season's end and the Didcot team drives went to Alain Prost and test driver Damon Hill instead for '93. Riccardo found a seat with Benetton-Ford, but this was very much second best – and in the twilight of his career it showed.

ALAIN PROST

1955-

All the very best, the standard-setting, drivers of every era have been "hot" from the day they first competed upon four wheels. Alain Prost is no exception. He was World Karting Champion in 1973 and in 1976 won the *Formule* Renault European title. In 1978 he added the European F3 crown and after setting startling times in a McLaren F1 test drive during the winter of 1979-80, he earned their No. 2 seat for the coming season alongside John Watson.

He scored World Championship points from his first two successive Grands Prix starts but the McLaren team was in sorry decline, and when Renault offered him a team place for 1981, Alain gladly grasped the chance. He quickly began winning Grand Prix races with Renault but unreliability, some driver errors and the team's relative lack of organization kept Prost and the World title apart.

He finally split from Renault late in 1983, but Renault's loss was the new McLaren International team's gain for 1984. MI was to use its new TAG Turbo-by-Porsche V6 engine that season in MP4/2 carbon-composite chassised cars which dominated for years to come. As Chief Engineer John Barnard put it, "Niki Lauda had been clearly dominant within the team – then suddenly Prost was on board and Niki found he had Concorde up his backside fighting to get past!"

Alain equaled the long-lived record of Jim Clark and

The most successful racing driver in Grand Prix history, this controlled, cerebral Frenchman with the looks of another Charles Aznavour, ended 1993 as motor racing's only four-time World Champion Driver, with only Juan Fangio having a better record with his five titles secured in less competitive times. In addition, Alain had long-since improved upon Jackie Stewart's all-time career best record of 27 GP victories and upon his retirement from race driving at the end of 1993 he had accumulated no fewer than 53 Grand Prix wins.

BELOW LEFT: Riccardo Patrese would become the most experienced driver in Formula 1 history as he surpassed the career race record of 176 Championship GPs held jointly by Graham Hill and Jacques Laffite. Riccardo outgrew his early ugly reputation in long years spent first with Brabham, then Williams. A sensitive man, he warmed to and rewarded the faith both teams demonstrated to him. Here he is in the 1989 Williams-Renault FW12C (FAR LEFT) and – less happily – in the twilight of his career in the 1993 Benetton-Ford.

RIGHT: Rising star – Alain Prost found his feet in Formula 1 with the turbocharged Renaults of 1981-83, winning nine Grands Prix.

James Hunt of seven World Championship GP victories in one season, yet team-mate Lauda still pipped him to the 1984 World title, by a dramatic half-point advantage. In 1985 Prost's superiority was rewarded by five victories and at last he won that elusive World title. Nobody since Jack Brabham in 1959-60 had achieved back-to-back titles. In 1986 Alain Prost did just that – World Champion again.

Nicknamed "The Professor" when at Renault, Alain was quite unspectacular to watch, smooth in the extreme, a driver of consummate touch, artistry and mechanical sympathy. In 1987, with the TAG Turbo engines past their development peak, he still salvaged three more GP wins to break Stewart's career record. But just as Lauda had found his pre-eminence overturned by Alain in 1984-85, so Prost's turn came in 1988 as Ayrton Senna joined McLaren who were to use the latest turbocharged Honda V6 engine.

Prost's relative caution when lapping backmarkers, and in the wet, were highlighted by Senna's perform-

RIGHT: After a sabbatical season through 1992 Prost returned to Formula 1 with Williams-Renault for '93, securing his fourth World title and setting a new career record of 52 Grand Prix victories. The high-tech car's carbon brakes glow red-hot under Alain's braking loads here in the British Grand Prix at Silverstone.

BELOW: In 1985 Alain Prost became the first Frenchman ever to win the World title. In 1986 he became the first man since Jack Brabham in 1959-60 successfully to defend his crown. Here he is set to win that year's Monaco Grand Prix in the McLaren-TAG Turbo MP4/2C.

ances in his sister car. Between them, the two McLaren-Honda stars won 15 of the 16 Championship GPs in 1988, but the title went to the Brazilian. Through 1989 with new 3.5-liter naturally-aspirated Honda V10 engines the rivalry between Prost and Senna grew, became bitter, and ended at Suzuka, Japan, as Alain plainly punted Senna off the road when being passed, in a maneuver which clinched the Frenchman's third World Championship title.

For 1990 Prost joined Nigel Mansell at Ferrari as joint number one, and his ability to mold a team around himself – only eclipsed by Senna's performance at McLaren – effectively aced-out Mansell in a season culminating again in Japan where Prost's hopes for a fourth World crown were sensationally shattered by Senna when he wiped out the Frenchman's Ferrari in the first corner.

By this time, allegedly darkly paranoid about Senna, politics and plots, Prost triggered changes at Ferrari for 1991 which ultimately exploded in his face. After public criticism of the faltering Italian team he was dismissed before the season-ending Australian GP.

A sabbatical season followed through 1992, but Alain remained motivated and with Renault and Elf backing took the No. 1 Williams drive for 1993. Handling the most technically advanced F1 car around, he clinched the fourth Drivers' World Championship title of a truly glittering racing career.

ABOVE: Alain Prost could be gallic charm personified. He brought a cool, measured, tactical and strategic approach to race driving and car development alike, and most race engineers enjoyed working with him. It all paid off as Alain became the most successful Formula 1 driver in racing history.

LEFT: But even "The Professor" occasionally cut kerbs.

RIGHT: One of the most highly motivated, aggressive, combative, and talented pure racing animals the sport has ever seen – *Il Leone* – "The British Lion" – Nigel Mansell in the 1989 Ferrari.

NIGEL MANSELL

1953-

If Graham Hill was a tough-minded, determined, dedicated sportsman who turned himself into a World Champion driver through sheer intense application, then Nigel Mansell is absolutely Graham's modern counterpart.

When, in 1992, Nigel became the first British World Champion Driver since James Hunt in '76, numerous now obscure characters who had once been his team-mates early in his career were left shaking their heads sorrowfully and recalling how, "I was always a second a lap quicker than him in sister cars."

But what they must have lacked was the incredible focus, and the intense support of his wife Rosanne for his ambitions. These, perhaps, have made Mansell into the worldwide superstar he subsequently became. The passage of years improved Mansell's race driving as surely as old wine matures within the cask and by the late 1980s he had become a truly formidable motor racing animal – a truly tigerish racer; one of the finest the sport has ever seen.

He abandoned a decent job with Lucas Aerospace in the early 1970s to dedicate himself to a racing career. He had learned the basics in karts, encouraged by his father, Eric, and scraped together money for a Formula Ford in which he notched his maiden win in 1976.

Even his house was sold to fuel his ambition. Pain and trauma did not deflect him. He broke his neck and damaged vertebrae in race accidents. Progressing painfully through Formula 3 into Formula 2, after such setbacks he would exercise to the point of collapse and will himself back to fitness.

In the summer of 1979 he won a test-drive with Team Lotus in which Colin Chapman recognized some intrinsic class. He became Lotus test and development driver, and Colin gave him a Grand Prix debut drive in the 1980 Austrian GP. More pain – fuel leaked into the car's cockpit, soaked through his overalls and chemical burns flayed his skin away – yet he drove on and on until the car's engine failed.

For 1981 he became Lotus No. 2 to Elio de Angelis. Lotus was in deep recession, Chapman suffered his fatal heart attack that December and Nigel lost his most important admirer. He stayed at Lotus through 1982-84 but seemed dogged by appalling luck – as accident prone off-circuit as on. His driving was sometimes desperate in its intensity.

He moved to Williams-Honda for 1985, and as that season progressed, a new Nigel Mansell emerged – just as intense, just as driven, in many respects just as theatrical, but now truly capable. At last he won at premier level – in the European GP at Brands Hatch, and again in South Africa. Through 1986, brimming with newfound confidence, he won five GPs and was poised to secure the World title in the final round – at Adelaide, Australia – only to suffer a spectacular rear tire explosion at around 190mph.

In 1987 he won six more GPs in spine-tingling style. With the Championship open only to himself and his team-mate Nelson Piquet, he crashed during practice in Japan, damaged his spine and missed the race – and the title for the second successive season.

Honda abandoned Williams for McLaren in 1988 – and Mansell, left with modest Judd V8 power that season, was unable to win a single race. He signed with Ferrari for 1989 and sensationally won his maiden race for the Italian team in Brazil, later adding a second McLaren-crushing win, in Hungary.

Often suspected of supposedly harboring a persecution complex, Mansell became estranged from Ferrari

through 1991 as Alain Prost appeared to gain precedence. A mid-season announcement of retirement was reversed only when old friends took him back to Williams, by this time equipped with Renault V10 engines and an ever-improving car design.

With Mansell driving in 1992, the Williams-Renaults proved virtually unbeatable, and at last – in Hungary – he clinched that World Championship title which had eluded him so long. But the Williams relationship collapsed, and Nigel left at season's end, abandoning Formula 1 in favor of Indycar racing in the U.S.

He made an establishment-shattering winning Indycar debut for the Carl Haas/Paul Newman Lola-Ford team at Surfer's Paradise, Australia, but then crashed heavily on the tight oval track at Phoenix, Arizona. Back injuries put him through more pain, and surgery, and another battle to recover, but he returned in time to miss victory only narrowly in his maiden Indianapolis 500-Miles classic – coming third. Five victories in subsequent races, with staggering displays upon the tight American oval tracks, set new standards within the competition and made him the first "rookie" ever to win the American Championship – and the first driver ever to secure the Formula 1 World title and the Indycar title in successive seasons. There is yet more to come from this most remarkable sportsman.

AYRTON SENNA

1960-

His wealthy father put Ayrton into a racing kart when he was barely four, and he had eight years' racing experience before beginning a full season of British Formula Ford racing in 1981. He learned fast – driving a Van Diemen to win two Championships with 12 wins from 20 starts. When money temporarily ran short, he returned to Brazil to drum up some more.

Back again for 1982 Formula Ford 2000 – Ayrton again achieved spectacular success. Into Formula 3 in 1983 he took the British Championship after a ferocious battle with Martin Brundle. He was given his F1 intro by Toleman-Hart in 1984, took a World Championship point second time out, and was second at Monaco after closing rapidly upon Prost's leading McLaren in falling rain only for the race to be prematurely ended by steward Jacky Ickx.

Senna knew his capabilities were greater than the Toleman team's potential and so signed for Lotus in '85. He allegedly endured vociferous censure from Toleman and their contractual difficulties took some sorting out.

With Lotus-Renault he won his maiden GP in a Portuguese downpour at Estoril and shone thereafter – always a front runner. In 1986 he established himself as the "qualifying King," taking nine pole positions, winning the Spanish GP at Jerez by a bare 100th-second from Mansell's Williams-Honda and winning at Detroit, too.

A great motor racing thinker – an uncompromising politician – the Brazilian's single-mindedness focused all his energies upon what would be good for Senna. Recognizing the superiority of Honda engines Lotus

A *Pãulistano* – from Sao Paulo, Brazil – Ayrton Senna is one of the most intensely committed and greatest racing drivers the world has ever seen. Men of such class rarely emerge – Tazio Nuvolari and Bernd Rosemeyer before World War II, Juan Manuel Fangio and Stirling Moss in the 1950s, Jim Clark and Jackie Stewart in the 1960s, and now Ayrton Senna.

As Stirling Moss puts it, the scheme of things arranges top sportsmen in a pyramid. There's a point on top, providing space for only one man. Just beneath that pinnacle there's room for maybe two or three. It is arguable today whether or not Ayrton Senna stands on that solitary top spot. He certainly ranks right up there with the Gods, enormously high indeed.

TOP LEFT: One of the most rapturously-received Grand Prix victories of all time was secured by Nigel Mansell driving his heart out on his home ground, before his home crowd, in the Williams-Renault FW14B at the British Grand Prix, Silverstone, 1992. He started from poll, set a new race lap record, won by a margin of over 20 seconds, and had to abandon his car after it was engulfed by his ecstatic supporters on the slowing-down lap.

LEFT: Team dominance – Mansell (1st) and Riccardo Patrese (2nd) after the Williams-Renault 1-2 which typified their 1992 season.

RIGHT: The greatest ever? The jury is still out on Ayrton Senna's potential claims to such a title but into the mid-90s he is certainly the standard-setter in sheer performance terms. He found his feet in Formula 1 – as here in 1986 – with Team Lotus and their turbocharged Renault V6 engines.

LEFT: In 1988 Senna and Prost provided McLaren-Honda with the most dominant World Championship-winning season in modern history as they drove their MP4/4 cars to victory in 15 of the year's 16 Grand Prix races, and Ayrton only lost the 16th when he collided with a backmarker two laps from home. Senna won eight GPs and the title.

BELOW: The brilliant Brazilian dominating the 1991 Monaco Grand Prix in McLaren's impeccably-prepared and potent latest – the Honda V12-engined MP4/6.

secured them for him for '87, but the Lotus-Honda 99T was no equal to the rival Williams-Honda and Ayrton won only twice.

McLaren then attracted Honda backing at Williams' expense, and Senna moved to them for 1988. Teamed with Alain Prost, here was a "superteam" indeed – and Ayrton did to Prost exactly what Alain had previously done to Niki Lauda and Keke Rosberg; he destroyed the established star's confidence and security.

Ayrton won the 1988 Imola, Canadian, Detroit, British, German, Hungarian, Belgian and Japanese GPs – a record eight victories in one season – and dominated both the Monaco and Italian GPs only for late errors to prevent him finishing. For 1989, with the new naturally-aspirated Honda V10 engines, a bitter rift

developed between Senna and Prost. The Frenchman is alleged to have believed the Brazilian had breached a "no passing" agreement at Imola. Senna supposedly dismissed Prost's claim, saying there had been no such agreement between them.

They virtually fought the long season between themselves. The World title lay between them alone in the Japanese GP, and as Prost was being overtaken, a collision occurred which led to Senna missing out a chicane. After winning the race upon the road Ayrton was accordingly excluded from the results, leaving Prost as World Champion.

For 1990 the feuding duo were in opposing teams – Prost with Ferrari, Senna with McLaren-Honda. Again the Championship lay between them at Suzuka, Japan. This time Senna rammed Prost's Ferrari in the tail entering the first corner, taking them both out and decided the World title – his third – in his own favor.

Ayrton stayed with McLaren into 1993, but after Honda's withdrawal and the substituiton of the latest Cosworth-Ford V8 engines, the old McLaren superiority had been lost and Senna had a terrific struggle to combat the Williams-Renaults. He still won five GPs before leaving McLaren at the end of the season to replace the retiring Prost at Williams-Renault, and into the mid-1990s he remains an awesome driving force.

ABOVE LEFT: Calm, clear, penetrating brown eyes laser-beaming out from that Brazilian-liveried crash helmet, Ayrton Senna, superstar, prepares for the latest battle on-circuit.

LEFT: Himself a sometime Monte Carlo resident during the Formula 1 racing season, Ayrton in the McLaren-Ford MP4/8 rounds Loew's Hairpin while winning the 1993 Monaco Grand Prix, bettering Graham Hill's long-lived record of five wins in the principality.

RIGHT: State of the art '93 – Gerhard Berger doing his best for Ferrari in the Monaco Grand Prix.

FAR RIGHT: Gerhard Berger – the lanky Austrian – accepted one of the last really big-money driver transfer deals (negotiated despite the recession) which took him from McLaren back to Ferrari for 1993, but in terms of results it represented a giant backward stride.

GERHARD BERGER

1959-

In an age when the leading racing drivers are stereotypically neat, compact, jockey-sized characters, the Austrian star Gerhard Berger physically towers head and shoulders above his peers.

Son of a road haulier, Berger found his feet in motor racing in saloon, Formula 3 and Formula 2 cars before making his Formula 1 debut – with a degree of BMW support – in the 1984 Austrian GP at Osterreichring handling one of irascible German team patron Gunther Schmid's ATS-BMW team cars. He retired that day, but then finished sixth in the Italian GP. Sadly, since he had not officially been entered in the FIA World Championship at the start of that season he was not given the Championship point he should have earned.

During that winter the 25-year-old seriously injured his neck. Any Formula 1 future he may have had seemed threatened. He worked hard upon a full recovery and reappeared in the Arrows-BMW team of 1985, showing further promise finishing in fifth place in South Africa and sixth in Australia. Benetton was emerging as a strong BMW-powered team and Gerhard joined them in '86, leading his home Grand Prix and then nursing his Pirelli tires non-stop all the long way through the Mexican GP to score an impressive first Grand Prix victory.

This confirmed the talent he had already signed over to Ferrari for 1987. He won the Japanese and Australian GPs and helped to return the charismatic Italian team to the top after two tough seasons in the doldrums. In 1988 Enzo Ferrari passed away, but at Monza for the Italian GP Berger kept his Ferrari close enough to the dominant Senna's McLaren-Honda to inherit victory when the Brazilian collided with a backmarker in the closing stages. The lucky Austrian won to a tumultuous reception from the ecstatic *tifosi*. His final season with Ferrari in 1989 then saw him struggling in Mansell's shadow, and he was injured in a fiery crash at Imola.

For 1990-92 he moved to McLaren, becoming Senna's team-mate, and cheerfully making the best of it – being given victory in the 1992 Japanese GP as Senna backed off before the finish line, in thanks for unstinting and gracious support through what had become the great Brazilian's third World Champion year. Into 1993 Berger returned to Ferrari, but their fortunes were dismal – and so were the chirpy, fun-loving Austrian's.

JEAN ALESI

1964-

A Frenchman of Sicilian parentage, Jean Alesi was the discovery of the 1989 Formula 1 World Championship season as he made the leap from second-division Formula 3000 to the Tyrrell team, and immediately proved his ability to give the finest established teams and drivers a terrific, competitive fright!

He finished fourth upon his F1 debut in his home Grand Prix in 1989 where two years earlier he had won the French national F3 title. He had driven an F3000 March for the Marlboro-sponsored ORECA team in '88, without great success, and for 1989 with the British-based Eddie Jordan team, who were renowned for nurturing bright young talent, he won the F3000 title in their Reynard-Mugen car winning at Pau, Birmingham and Spa. He then hurdled straight into the Tyrrell F1 team and proved spectacularly fast if occasionally equally spectacularly brainless.

In 1990 he secured second places at Phoenix and Monaco in the Tyrrell-Ford, but as the team's fortunes faded so Ferrari offered him a place for 1991, and he jumped at the chance as would any fine driver with Italian blood in his veins. Sadly, he joined a team riven by politics and deep in the embrace of profound technical difficulties which would smother Alesi's undoubted flair, fire and skill.

He persevered with perennially limited Ferrari machinery through 1992-93 – learning the intrinsic skills of racing car set-up, preparation, and racecraft along the way; a character-building exercise which must pay dividends once the machinery matches his innate promise and skill within the cockpit.

ABOVE: Gallic flair and *brio* combined with a family background of Sicilian sinew and toughness – Jean Alesi, the French Formula 3000 star rocketed to Formula 1 celebrity with Tyrrell in 1989-90 before moving to Ferrari. His fortunes then faltered with the historic Italian team (LEFT).

INDEX

Acknowledgments

The author and publisher
would like to thank David
Eldred, the designer; Stephen
Small, the editor and picture
researcher; Nicki Giles and
Veronica Price for production;
Ron Watson for preparing the
index; and the individuals and
institutions listed below for
supplying the pictures.

Chris Bennett, pages: 1,
66(bottom right), 69,
70(bottom), 76(both), 77(bottom
left)
**Neill Bruce/The Peter
Roberts Collection, pages:**
17, 24
David Hodges, pages:
39(bottom), 40(bottom), 53, 56,
62, 63(top), 64(bottom),
65(bottom left), 67, 68, 73, 74,
75
**National Motor Museum,
pages:** 8-9, 13(bottom),
16(both), 17, 23, 44, 49(top), 61,
63(bottom), 66(bottom left),
70(top), 71, 72(both), 77(bottom
right), 78(top)
**Doug Nye/The GP Picture
Library, pages:** 2-3, 4-5, 6, 7,
9(bottom), 10, 11, 12, 13(top), 14,
15, 18, 20(bottom), 21(both), 22,
25(both), 26, 27(both), 28,
29(both), 30(both), 31, 32, 33,
34-5, 35(bottom), 36, 37(both),
38, 39(top), 40(top), 41, 42, 43,
45(both), 46, 47, 48, 49(bottom),
50, 51, 52, 54(both), 55, 57,
58(both), 59, 60(both), 64(top),
65(bottom right)